Latvian Folktales

RETOLD BY
Astrida Barbins-Stahnke & Carma Stahnke

ILLUSTRATED BY
Laura Belevica

ISBN: 978-1-7361306-2-9 (Paperback)
        978-1-7361306-4-3 (Hardcover)

A.B.S. Publishing
www.authorastridastahnke.com

Contents

INTRODUCTION

Latvia lies on the eastern shore of the Baltic Sea and, with Estonia to the north and Lithuania to the south, is one of the three Baltic States. Due to their geographical location, natural beauty and plentiful resources, these countries experienced repeated cycles of foreign invasion, occupation, and oppression throughout their long history. They also enjoyed times of freedom that allowed progressive development and hope for national independence. These rich and complex events give context to this collection of folktales.

Originally settled by the ancient Balts, modern-day Latvia came under Viking overlordship in the 9th century. German-speaking forces from the west eventually established dominance, and Christianization of the northern tribes began in 1198, when Bishop Berthold of Hannover landed in the Gulf of Riga. By 1230, Latvia had been conquered by Teutonic knights and remained enserfed peasantry under the German landowning class. The country was then partitioned between Poland and Sweden during the mid-16th to early 18th centuries. After the Great Northern War (1700-1711), Imperial Russia gained control over the region, with German nobility remaining as landlords over the indigenous population. Each state became an independent republic after World War I (1918), only to be overtaken by the Soviet Union after World War II (1945). The Baltic States remained under Soviet control until 1991 when, after much bloodshed and immeasurable human suffering, they gained independence once again.

During the pre-Christian era, Norse paganism, a combination of legends and highly varied Baltic mythology, was prevalent throughout the region. During the centuries of oppression that followed, the once tribal people, illiterate and forcefully subordinated, clung to their old beliefs while giving obeisance to the Christian (Catholic) overlords who enslaved and exploited them. They ridiculed the language (oldest among

Indo-European languages) and kept natives out of the guilds and schools. Any national aspirations were denied and even criminalized. The abuses, camouflaged in symbols, folktales, proverbs, songs, and pagan myths, were secretly passed on by word of mouth for generations, until the abolishment of serfdom in the mid-1800s.

Despite this oppression, heroes emerged and became catalysts for change. These were typically young men, educated by their masters and allowed the privilege of studying abroad. Among them appeared newspaper editors, poets, composers, merchants, and entrepreneurs of many kinds. Some German clergy even joined in, defending human rights, opening schools, and bringing a buried, romanticized antiquity back to life. They established nearly democratic kingdoms and set out to educate and enlighten the laboring, oppressed natives. This gave rise to a powerful movement known as the National Awakening (1850-1880s). During these years, oppressed men and women awoke as if from a deep sleep and sought their rights to education and freedom.

Among the educated, native-Latvian youth, Krišjānis Barons (1835-1923) stands out as the supreme collector and classifier of folk songs (the dainas). He walked the whole country and sought out older populations from whom he learned songs, tales, true stories, myths, and legends. Barons (and later others) classified and disseminated these works through newspapers and then published them in six large volumes between 1894 and 1915. As founder of Jaunlatvieši (the New Latvians), he established the study of folklore as legitimate subject matter, a view still present today. Consequently, ancient wisdom has never gone out of style and has become a central part of the Latvian identity. Folklore remains rich source material for all the arts, both classical and popular.

The folktales we selected for this book are like tiny amber chips on the white sandy beaches, tossed by stormy waters from the depths of the Baltic Sea. Each piece is a gem that tells its own unique story. The tales also share similarities, set within agrarian landscapes and teaching lessons on patience, gratitude, discontent and the spirit of rebellion and adventure. Of course, as in folktales the world over, animal characters are masked humans who embody universal behaviors and truths.

Latvia is a small country whose history is greatly defined by invasion and occupation of larger, more powerful forces. It is therefore no surprise that we see folktales that champion smaller characters who take on larger, more powerful characters, reducing them to ridicule through cunning and cleverness. We also see humble gods who show up just in time to help the innocent: Dieviņš, disguised as a farmer, goes about blessing the fields or miraculously rescuing the deserving from a life of poverty; Māra and Laima, earth and fortune goddesses, teach and protect the innocent and punish the guilty; Velniņš, the devil, is a trickster, an acrobat who confuses us and leads us astray.

Saule, the sun, is another key figure. In Baltic mythology, the sun is a feminine force: the light, the comforter, the fertile mother who nurtures the world. From the smallest insect to the biggest bear, she shines on the just and the unjust and sends her helpers, the earth, water, and wind daughters, robed in fog and mist, to those in need. The male counterpart is the feared Pērkonis or "thunder," who strikes with lightning bolts.

These pagan deities have become embedded in the Latvian psyche and are evident in a shared respect for nature: honoring the rights of wild animals, preserving the nests of migrating birds, and understanding the healing properties of various herbs and grasses. Children are taught not to pick a flower for fun, but to pass it on as a gift, with love and welcome— even to strangers. They learn the names of plants, trees, and many other natural entities, as if each were given to us to cherish and protect, for we are no greater than the least of these.

As this book is meant to "teach and delight," it is not limited to any age group, race or nation. If there were any specific reason for our choosing these folktales, perhaps it was to tell whoever wants to listen that there, far in the north, tribes once lived, ancestors to many of us. We are here because they knew how to survive the worst of times and enjoy the best through song, dance, stories, laughter, and reverence for Mother Earth, who gives her blessings freely to all who love and protect her.

Astrida Barbins-Stahnke
Carma Stahnke

Artist's Message to Our Readers

Given the current, complex age of crisis, overwhelming stress and high-speed, super-efficient, automated lives, you may wonder why you should care about folktales. What can an old story really teach you? Well, I happen to know that Latvian folktales have EVERYTHING to do with your life IF you know how to read them. Let me explain.

Just as a simple flower can have a magic, medicinal power to heal you as an herb, a folktale can heal and soothe your soul. It helps you to see your life with new eyes because of the symbols and metaphors hidden within. All you need to do is simply connect the dots. And so this book holds seven dots – seven keys to this universe, to these seven symbolic galaxies. And the seven keys are seven lenses through which you can see any folktale. Seven, by the way, is a special number. It is no coincidence that the world was created in seven days, that there are seven sacraments, seven different systems of thought, seven chakras, seven layers of skin.

I see this book almost like the tip of a magical iceberg, an appetizer of knowledge that you can savor, like jars of different herbs that you can pick and choose; here is a selection of ancient Latvian treasures, kernels of wisdom, with which to brew a cup of tea. This book invites you to discover the kernels at your own pace and in any order you may wish. Just know that there are seven galaxies, each with its own system, scope, and message.

The first group of stories presented here talks about home and safety. The action happens within a closed interior/domestic environment. These are fairytales about cats and mice and relationships between different characters within the home: coexistence, trust, fragile balance and what happens when that breaks loose. Inevitable chaos or even peril may ensue.

The second group explores the idea of family, coupled with ancient understanding of who and what makes up a family. Here you have tales where such concepts as luck and greed are personified; for example, luck may suddenly appear, bringing a surprising message or pivot the persona's course of action in an unexpected direction. As these abstract, uncontrollable concepts are humanized and, in your imagination, become familiar individuals whom you can see and talk to. You can have a conversation with "Lady Luck" or an argument with "Guilt."

The third group depicts the ways of the world. In these tales, animals have different characteristics and viewpoints through which a lesson is conveyed, and this wisdom is not simply about being the biggest or fastest animal in the end. These tales are about how you use your unique traits, your wit, and cunning. They employ the hierarchy of animals to explain, for example, that, once you leave home, once you leave the safety of your environment and your extended family of spirits and traits, you will face other creatures. And they will come in all shapes and sizes, large and small, all having peculiar traits you would have to be aware of in order to protect yourself and survive in perilous situations. At this juncture, you must figure out where you fit, what you have to offer, and what you can contribute. If you are a smaller animal, you must use your wits in order to win the race and come out victorious and grown in self-confidence, ready to face the next challenge.

The fourth category conveys the wisdom that can be found in nature and how nature can become an ally, a guide. A bird can teach you about patience; a garden can teach you about resilience. These are all lessons that must be learned as we journey through life.

The fifth category is the universe of magic. Each tale contains a key element, a key artifact: magic wings, a magic ring, or some other object that gives you special power. It's a symbol, but it is also a life secret that each one of us must find on our own. But where do we find it? How do we recognize and use it? How do we apply it? How do we achieve what we desire with this element that we can't really explain, or understand or know where it is? Here we may find ourselves lost in the invisible and imaginative crossroads. Where to go and what road to take is a chance-taking mystery. Dare the girl dive into unknown depths with a serpent?

Dare a youth trust a magic steed to scale a treacherous tower? And what would happen if both did nothing? And how would one prepare to make the right decision? How do we deal with our inner drives and the inexplicable mystery all around us? The poet says, "Look into your heart!"

The sixth category gives you clues about where that magic can be found. It resides mainly in your vast internal world. After you leave your home and expand your understanding of who you are, given your identity, your purpose, your extended family values, you face the world of creatures and animals and find your place in it. As you navigate that world, you gain wisdom from nature and eventually release control by allowing the mystery and magic to play out their roles. By the end of the day, you realize that all the answers are indeed within you, that you must examine your internal world and find the answer there. And that search will require wisdom and strength. It will be a part of life's journey on our beautiful, fragile Earth.

The seventh category represents an even higher consciousness, a higher wisdom, an exploration of the importance of awareness, of mantras, and of being present and centered in the moment. That is ultimately the only thing you can do. You may think you have control, but you have to release that understanding and realize that it is both true and not true. All you have is your life, your internal emotional world and your physical body. How you live depends on this castle that holds your body and soul.

All of this is hidden between the lines in Latvian folktales, passed down through generations. At first glance, they may seem to be just old stories, but they are actually gems of wisdom. And that's why this is a book worth reading. I hope you enjoy this wonderful selection of treasures. And when you're done, go explore the meadow. See what you find!

Laura Belevica

Ej, dieviņ, tu pa priekšu,
Es tavās pēdiņās;
Neļauj man iet to celiņu,
Kur aizgāja ļauni ļaudis.

Please, dear God, walk ahead.
I shall follow in Thy footsteps.
Do not let me take the path
Where the wicked people walk.

The Golden Apple

(Zelta ābols)

Once upon a time, the king of a certain land had a beautiful daughter who suddenly became very sick. All kinds of doctors and wise men were called, but no one could help her. At last a sorcerer was consulted and told the king that the girl needed a golden apple. "That will cure her immediately," he said.

That same hour the king sent out a proclamation, saying that whoever brought him a golden apple would be greatly rewarded: The king's daughter would become his bride!

And so it happened that in the same land lived a farmer who had three sons. Two were thought to be very clever, while the third was nicknamed Muļķītis, or "Simpleton," because people thought he wasn't very smart. Still, this must have been a special family, because the very next morning, after the king's announcement, a miracle happened: In front of the farmhouse stood an apple tree with three golden apples!

Excited but confused, the farmer scratched his head, wondering what he should do. He looked up at the tree and counted, "One, two, three golden apples. Same as on my family tree! I have three sons. I'm the strong tree, they the shining fruit." Then a ray of sun shone from heaven down into his eyes, and he took it as a sign: "I know exactly what to do. I'll pick the apples, give one to each of my sons and send them, one at a time, to the castle." And that is what he did. Three mornings in a row he commanded: "Go, my son, and try your luck!"

First went the eldest son. He took a piece of bread, put a golden apple in his pocket, and set out on the road. He walked and walked until he came to a deep forest. He went into the woods even though it was getting dark. As the evening descended upon him, he felt great hunger rattling his stomach. So he sat down next to a tree, pulled out his piece of bread, bit into it, and began to chew. Suddenly, as if from the ground, an old man popped up beside him.

"Please, oh please, give me a little crust of your bread! I am very hungry." But the tough young man did not care. He never shared anything with anybody. Instead, he gave the old man a piece of his mind: "Why don't you go find a job? Then you won't have to beg."

Hearing that, the old man disappeared without a word.

The next morning, the eldest son arrived at the castle, and the servants took him to the king.

"What do you want?" the king asked.

"I want to marry the princess," he declared. "I brought you a golden apple, so this is my just reward."

The king looked him over rather suspiciously and said, "Show it to me!"

"Sure," said the eldest and put his hand in his pocket, ready to pull out the apple of pure gold. But – oh, no! What a shock! Instead of an apple, he pulled out a snake, curled up and hissing. The king became furious and commanded his guards: "Throw this rogue into the dungeon!" The guards put a rope around the young man's neck and drug him away.

The next day, the middle son went to seek his fortune. He also packed a piece of bread in his bag, put a golden apple in his pocket, and set off on the same road through the forest. He walked until the evening darkness fell upon him. He, likewise, became hungry, pulled out his chunk of bread, and bit into it. Suddenly, from neither here nor there, the same old man appeared. "Please, sir," he moaned, "can I have some of your bread?" But the middle son did not care and had no intention of sharing: "You should be working instead of begging. You know the saying: 'If you don't work, you don't eat.'"

Hearing that, the old man vanished into the darkness.

In the morning, the middle son came to the castle, and the servants took him to the king. Even more irritated than the day before, the king demanded, "What do you want?"

"I-I wa-want to marry the p-princ-cess," he stuttered. "I-I b-brought you a g-golden ap-p-le."

"Let me see it!" the king said harshly.

"Sure," the young man said, standing tall and putting his hand into his pocket, eager to pull out the apple of pure gold. But – guess what? Instead of the nice, hard apple, he was holding a slimy, hissing, spewing snake. This was too much for the king. He thought these farm boys were trying to humiliate him and his daughter.

"Throw that stammering fool into the dungeon with his brother – snakes and all!"

On the third day it was Muļķītis, the youngest son's, turn to go and seek his fortune. His father was worried, since his two other boys had not returned, but Muļķītis put the bread and the golden apple in his pocket and set out anyway.

He walked and walked until he came to the same forest and the same tree. He felt a bit afraid all alone in the darkness with the strange noises, but he was hungry and decided to eat. No sooner had he bitten into his bread, when – guess who? – was suddenly beside him, begging for a crust of bread. *Muļķītis*, glad to have some company, said, "Sure! Here, uncle, eat up! I'm not that hungry."

The old man thanked *Muļķītis* for his kindness and took the bread.

"You're a good boy. Keep being kind to the poor, and all will go well for you in life."

In the morning *Muļķītis* woke up bright and early and hurried to the castle. Reluctantly, the servants took him to the king.

"What do you want?"

"I want nothing," answered *Muļķītis*. "I just brought you a golden apple so you can cure the princess – according to your own decree, your majesty." Not the least bit afraid, he smiled at the king and his guards.

But the king, mad as ever, ranted and raved, ready to throw *Muļķītis* into the dungeon with his brothers. *Muļķītis* had no idea why the king was so angry. He reached into his pocket and pulled out a golden apple.

Now it was the king's turn to feel foolish. He said he did not mean what he'd said. He had dealt with two rogues two days in a row and could not handle a third. Besides, his daughter now had a rash, and she was getting sicker by the day. So he grabbed the magic apple and hurried to the princess.

The king burst threw her door and tossed her the apple. She jumped up, caught the golden apple and was cured instantly!

"She's as healthy as ever!" said the doctor after examining her.

Now the wedding was supposed to take place, but *Muļķītis* did not want to get married.

"What would I do with a gilded princess, and how would I manage the castle?" he said, shaking his head. He glanced at the pretty princess, playing with the apple as a toy. He knew she would not like to climb a real apple tree and pick a bushel of real apples.

"But how should I reward you?" asked the king.

"If it would please your majesty," *Muļķītis* bowed, "set my brothers free. We have to go home because there is work to do, and our father should not be left alone for so long. We have no mother," he added sadly.

"All right, all right," said the king, and threw some copper coins his way. He was only too glad to see the brothers leave his castle so he and his daughter could live in peace.

But *Muļķītis* could hardly wait for the next time he could help someone in distress.

"I may not be as clever as you two, but I believe in helping people when I can and not expecting anything in return. Kindness is its own reward," he told his brothers on the way home. And they listened to him with great respect.

The Small Animal War

(Dzīvnieku karš)

One day a dog and a fox got into an argument about who had the stronger friends.

"Look at my pal, the bear. He is one of the bravest animals in the forest. Nothing frightens him!" boasted the fox.

"Ha! My buddy the bull can plow a whole field by himself. He's clearly tougher than your bear," snapped the dog.

"But what about my friend the boar?" said the fox.

"And what about my friend the horse?" said the dog.

Realizing they weren't getting anywhere, they decided to resolve their argument by staging a battle. They agreed that each would select two of their strongest friends to face off in a clearing at the edge of the woods.

The fox, at the agreed-upon time, arrived at the battlefield with his two soldiers, the boar and the bear. The dog was running late because he couldn't round up his army in such a short time. The horse had made excuses, neighing that the farmer had him working hard already, and he could not go. Then the dog went to the bull, but he, too, refused, mooing that he had a horn-ache.

The dog wondered what he should do next. The time for battle was fast approaching, but he had no army. Finally, not getting any help from the horse or the bull, he went to the cat and the rooster.

"How would you two like to come to battle with me? This is our chance to put that fox in his place and be heroes of the forest!" Having been annoyed by the fox many times before, the cat and rooster were glad to be of service.

"Okay troops, let's march! Make as much noise as you can. We'll show that fox who has the better army!"

Running to the battlefield, the dog barked and howled, the cat meowed and scratched, and the rooster flapped and crowed. Never was such a cacophony heard in this usually peaceful forest.

In the meantime, the fox and his troops were growing impatient.

"Bear, climb up that pine tree and see if our opponents are on their way," the fox ordered.

The bear quickly climbed as high as he could. Seeing the dog, the cat and the rooster heading their way, he called down to the fox: "They're coming fast!" Soon the whole forest shook with the oncoming army's noise, getting closer and closer to the battlefield.

The fox called to the bear, "Come down from that tree and line up for the fight!"

"No! I will not climb down! I'll stay right where I am, so those crazy soldiers don't get me."

The boar, hearing this dreadful racket, became so scared that he started burrowing into a nearby swamp to hide. He dug completely into the mud and covered himself with moss. Only the tip of his tail was sticking out.

Left by himself, the fox was also too scared to fight. How could he possibly take on the enemy all by himself? So he snuck off into the woods, leaving the bear in the tree and the boar in the swamp.

Finally, the dog arrived with the cat and the rooster, ready to fight. They looked around, up in the trees and in the bushes, but could not find the opposing army. Since the dog was dog-tired from the entire ordeal, he decided to catch a little snooze – he was in no hurry to fight if no one else was. The rooster did what roosters do: He beat his wings together and loudly crowed in irritation.

Hearing the rooster's angry calls, the boar became so frightened that he shook all over. Even his tail, which was sticking out of the ground, wiggled. This caught the eye of the cat. She stood very still, eyeing what she thought was a mouse. And as soon as she was ready, she pounced, and she got it!

The cat did not realize that a whole boar was hiding underground until he jumped out, covered in mud, and ran off into the woods. The cat had scared the big wild boar out of his wits! This also scared the cat. She scampered up the tallest pine tree she saw. Poor kitty did not know that the bear was already up there. Hearing the cat climbing quickly toward him, the bear thought he was being attacked and fell backwards out of the tree like a huge sack of grain. He rolled over, picked himself up, and let his huge paws carry him off deep into the woods. The forest was quiet once more.

The next day the fox and the dog met again.

"How about we forget all this war business?" asked the fox. "I think all our friends are strong in their own way."

"Agreed!" said the dog, and the two never spoke of the incident again.

A Story about Patience

(Pasaka par pacietību)

O nce upon a time, a farmer's wife prepared her loom to make a long cloth and began to weave. She wove and wove, but no matter how hard she worked, she never seemed to make any progress. Imagining she would be sitting at her loom forever, she became upset and ran out of the house crying.

"I can't do anything right! Other wives weave the most beautiful curtains and tablecloths. I can't even make a dishrag!"

When she came to the edge of the woods, she slowed down and sat on a log, feeling very sorry for herself. Then, out of the corner of her eye, she noticed a tiny bird pecking at a large rock. Surprised, she asked, "Little bird, how on earth are you going to break apart that big rock all by yourself?"

"A little bit now, a little bit then, and in good time, the rock will be broken into pieces," the busy bird answered and kept on pecking.

"If such a tiny bird believes he can break up such a big rock, then I too in time will finish my cloth," she thought.

Drying her eyes, she stood up and looked around. Birdsong filled the air; all the little forest creatures seemed to be moving and working. Large and small ants dragged pine needles to their mounds; a woodpecker hammered the bark of an oak tree; a worm poked out of its tunnel. "Life isn't easy," she realized. She knew she had to either keep running or go home and face her dilemma. She decided to return to her cabin in the woods.

The next morning, after a good night's sleep and a healthy breakfast, she sat down at her loom and picked up where she had left off. Determined to see the job through, she decided to weave a segment every day, just like the bird pecking at the rock bit by bit. And that is exactly what she did.

She kept on weaving until, at last – oh, what a joy! – the cloth was finished. And it was beautiful! Even the little bird must have thought so, for he often came to sing at the woman's window, and she happily rewarded him with handfuls of bread crumbs.

The House Mouse and the Field Mouse

(Mājas pele un lauku pele)

One sunny day, a house mouse crawled out of her hole in the floorboard and ran to the cornfield called *Sildruva* to visit her sister, a field mouse.

"Good day to you!" greeted the visitor. "Do you remember me, your one and only sister?"

"Of course, I do!" said the surprised field mouse, who was very happy. "How could I forget you? But did you find your way okay? You didn't get lost, did you?"

"No, I didn't get lost," the house mouse said as she looked around. "Boy, it sure smells out here. What are those weeds over there?" she asked, making a sour face.

"Those aren't weeds! Those are my sprouting seeds of grain," the field mouse said proudly. "I have been tending to them all season. When they're ready, I'll make my bread for winter."

"Oh, goodness," squeaked the town mouse. "What kind of bread do you eat?" And she looked down on her crouching gray sister. "I'd starve to death just eating home-made bread. I tell you what, sister. I live on much better stuff: in the morning – meat; at noon – fat; in the evening – cream. And all that is right outside my hole. I just have to take it. Oh, I tell you, my life is grand compared to yours! Come home with me, and you'll see how to live without work."

"All right. I'll go with you," the field mouse doubtfully replied.

The two sisters took the secret tunnel into town, the house mouse leading the way boldly and bravely, while her skinny gray sister timidly followed. At last they reached the passage that led into the house. Since it was still light, they scurried under the floorboards and crouched, waiting for night, when all would be quiet. Then they crawled out of their hiding place, but before going on, the house mouse asked Mr. Cricket, "Is the cat at home?"

"No, he's gone to Riga with a load of mouse skins."

"Good! Time to act," said the house mouse. "Sister, you stay here by the hole. I'll bring the food up, and you take it inside."

But when the house mouse had taken a few steps forward – POUNCE! The cat was on top of her! Luckily, she escaped into her hole just in time, or else her grand life would have been swallowed up for sure.

"Oh, this is nothing," the house mouse tried to calm her sister. "Since our plan didn't work, we'll try something else," she said casually, sprucing herself up a bit. "We'll go for the bacon in the smokehouse."

They scurried through crooked and straight passageways, above ground and below, but when they came out at the end, there was the farmer with his hunting dog who only sniffed once before taking off after the mice – barking, whining, and scratching at the tiny hole the farmer hadn't noticed before. Again the mice had safely escaped, but the field mouse had had enough trouble and excitement.

"I'm done!" she said, standing on her hind legs. "I'm going home. I've relearned the lesson I had almost forgotten: 'Be content with what you have and make the most of it,'" she said and, looking at her sister with pity, added, "I'd rather eat my sprouts in safety than your delicacies in fear." Then she bristled so that she looked bigger than her sister, who was still trembling, and said, "I gather and plant my seeds all by myself. I work hard, while you live off others. That's no good. Good-bye, my sister!"

The Little White Dog

(Baltais sunītis)

Once there was a stepmother who treated her stepdaughter worse than a dog. No matter what the stepdaughter did, she could never please her.

One day, the stepdaughter was told that the pails were empty, and she must go to the well, draw the water, fill them, and carry them to the house. The poor girl was not strong enough to do all that, so she sat at the well, crying. Suddenly a little white dog appeared beside her: "If you will have me for a husband, I will make sure the water gets to the house." What could the girl do but agree?

"You just go back home and the pails will be there. As for our agreement, I'll give you time to prepare for our wedding." The girl, a bit confused, returned home and found the pails waiting for her.

"What a surprise," her stepmother said. "If you can do this so easily, I'm going to give you even more work from now on."

The stepdaughter sighed, knowing there was no use arguing with her. "Maybe that little white dog will come and save me one day," she thought.

But time passed and, with all her work, the stepdaughter forgot about the dog. Years later, a nice but poor man proposed to her. She didn't want to get married, but her stepmother insisted: "You need to go off and live in your own house. I have enough to worry about without you getting in my way." So the stepdaughter agreed to the poor man's proposal.

On the eve of the wedding, the bride- and groom-to-be and their families came to the stepdaughter's home for the customary dinner.

Suddenly, among the guests, the little white dog appeared, whining and jumping up and down on his hind legs, but hardly anyone noticed him. They headed into the house and sat down to eat, leaving the dog outside. As soon as they picked up their forks and knives, they heard someone singing outside:

> *Dearest girl, let me in,*
> *Me a wee, little man! -*
> *Think of that bygone day*
> *And your promise at the well!*

The guests looked at each other curiously, and a couple went out to see who was singing this strange song on the eve of the stepdaughter's wedding. "It's a little white dog!" laughed one of the guests. "Let the poor fellow in," said another. They opened the door, and the dog ran inside. Seeing the groom sitting next to his bride, he repeated his song:

> *Dearest girl, set me by you,*
> *Me a wee, little man!*
> *Think of that bygone day*
> *And your promise at the well!*

"What a funny little dog!" the groom said. "Well, what harm can there be if he joins us? Come, lie down here." The dog lay down at the bride's feet and was very good and quiet throughout the dinner.

In the morning, the guests again gathered, this time for the wedding-day breakfast. As they were going inside, the dog suddenly appeared and loudly sang his song. "Oh, let him in. He's such a cute little thing!" said one of the guests.

Now, by this time, the bride was starting to remember that day at the well. She wasn't very happy to be marrying the poor man, but marrying a dog wasn't a good idea either: "It would be pretty embarrassing to admit I accepted a proposal from a dog. I'll just see if I can keep him occupied until after the ceremony."

So the bride set down a plate with one sausage and one egg, thinking this would keep the dog quiet. And that suited him fine; he even lay down for a short snooze after his meal. While he was sleeping, the bride, groom, and guests headed to the church on the hill. When the dog woke up and saw he was alone, he ran out the door and, hiding in tall grasses along the road, raced to the church.

When he caught up with the bride's carriage, prancing around on his two back legs, he sang a variation of the old song:

> *Dearest girl, take me with you,*
> *Me a wee, little man!*
> *Think of that bygone day*
> *And the promise by the well!*

The bridegroom smiled and said, "Up, boy!" And the dog jumped into the wagon, happy as could be to ride to the church with the bride.

All the guests pulled into the courtyard and headed inside. The "wee little man" followed at their heels. After some hymns were sung and prayers said, the bride and groom walked slowly up the aisle to the altar. As the preacher was about to start the marriage ceremony, the dog suddenly rose up on his hind legs again and urgently sang at the top of his lungs:

> *Dearest girl, marry me,*
> *Me a wee, little man!*
> *Think of that lovely day*
> *And the promise that you made!*

Now the preacher became quite excited, for in his whole life he had never seen such a wedding party. Wiping the sweat from his brow with a handkerchief, he asked in a shaky voice, "Dear girl, what promise did you make? Please tell me quickly! We have to discover what this singing dog is all about."

The blushing bride now had to tell the whole story, from beginning to end. The guests listened with disgust as she described her stepmother's cruelty. Ashamed, the stepmother ran out of the church and back home, locking the door behind her.

The bridegroom, being a sensible man, asked, "Why didn't you tell me all this in the beginning? I can't marry a girl who is promised to another, even if the other is a dog. It just wouldn't be right." He strode out of the church, leaving the bride crying at the altar.

Then, as if this day couldn't get more odd, a most elegant coach driven by eight horses pulled up and stopped at the church door. A livery man stepped down from the driver's seat and opened the coach door. The little white dog jumped in, and seconds later, out the other door, stepped a handsome prince!

The guests couldn't believe their eyes as he walked into the church, down the aisle, and up to the altar. He stood next to the poor, bewildered bride and took her hand. The preacher thought that the angel Gabriel had flown down from heaven to wed the poor, abused orphan. He quickly married the couple, afraid the prince would turn back into a dog at any moment.

The ceremony over, the wedding party drove to the prince's castle where the couple lived happily ever after. To this day, no one has ever seen a stranger wedding day. Although some of the details have become confused, the people all agree that even the most unlikely of prospects can turn into a handsome prince. Now, young ladies from miles around take their pails to the well, even if they don't need any water.

The Farmer and the Frog

(Saimnieks un varde)

In the autumn, as snow was already starting to cover the earth, it so happened that a farmer, while ploughing his field for winter rye, almost stepped on a half-frozen frog.

"What's this?" the farmer asked in surprise.

"Dear man," croaked the frog, "would you please let me take shelter in your home? I'm afraid I will freeze to death out here."

At first, the farmer was in no mood to listen to the poor little creature, but then she promised to generously reward him for his pains. So he carefully wrapped her up, took her home, and put her in a slop bucket. And there the frog stayed all winter long.

When spring arrived and all the animals, worms, bees, mosquitos and even children awoke and came out of their nooks and crannies, the farmer nudged the frog, who was sleeping in her puddle under some old leaves: "Hey! Wake up! Time to give me my reward like you promised. Remember?"

Slowly the frog opened her eyes, stretched her legs, rose up on her two feet and said: "In the forest, near the stream, you will find a crooked linden tree. Its bark is very soft and pliable and has magic powers. Pull off two strips of this bark and make yourself a pair of vīzes. Put them on after a hard day's work, and your feet won't hurt anymore."

The farmer thanked the frog, lifted her out of the bucket, and took her outside to the edge of the pond, where she happily joined her sisters.

17

The farmer did as the frog had told him. He wore the magic vīzes every night, and his feet never ached again. He told his neighbors this secret and, since then, people have been making slippers from soft, pliable linden bark.

The Stubborn Little Bird

(Iecirtīgais putniņš)

Once upon a time, three friends lived in a small hut in the woods: a bird, a mouse, and a sausage. It was a harmonious household, for each had his job to do, and each worked the best he could. Every morning Bird brought sticks from the forest, Mouse carried water from the well, and Sausage kept house. When the wood and water were brought in, Sausage would make a fire in the fireplace, put the kettle on the hob, and cook the soup. So that the broth would taste good, she would jump into the kettle, turn herself around three times and jump out again. This made the soup better than the best, with just the right amount of fat and spice.

And so the three friends lived happily for some time.

But then, one morning, Bird got a bug in his ear and refused to go to the forest to gather kindling: "Why should I be the one to carry wood every morning? My beak hurts, and I can't fly straight! It's not fair that I have the hardest chore. You two have it easy." His feathers grew to one big ruffle and fluff: "Let's trade jobs. I'll carry the water. Mouse, you can cook. Sausage, you get the wood for the fire."

"Say," squeaked Mouse to Sausage, "can any good come of this?"

"I doubt it," sizzled Sausage, "but we better go along to keep the peace."

At last, for the sake of domestic tranquility, all agreed to give Bird's idea a try.

The next day, very early, Sausage got up and tumbled towards the forest to collect the kindling. But she had not even made it to the edge when she came face to face with a dog, out on his morning walk. Barking with excitement, he chomped down on Sausage and swallowed her in one bite. She tasted so good!

At the same time, Bird went to the well for water. He filled the pail and had almost pulled it up to the top when he lost hold of the handle. The heavy bucket rolled back into the well, pulling him down with it. He got tangled up in the rope and drowned.

Mouse stayed home, trying to cook the way Sausage had. As the soup started bubbling, she jumped into the kettle, but – oh, how terrible! – the poor thing didn't have a chance to turn around even once. The boiling heat swallowed her up before she could even make a squeak.

And so, the inhabitants of the small hut all lost their lives because of the foolish bird whose selfishness destroyed their happy home.

The Mean Old Woman and the Little Girl

(Skopā sieva un meitiņa)

In an old rundown hut in the woods there once lived a mean old woman and a little girl. They were very poor and never had enough to eat. When the food ran out, the woman lost all patience. She blamed the little girl for all their problems and would pull her hair and slap her face. She didn't care if the girl sniffled quietly, afraid to speak. She only cared about her growling stomach.

"We don't have any bread in the house, not even a crumb," she griped. "Don't just sit there! Go find us some food!"

Terrified, the girl had no choice but to obey. Out in the cold, she wondered what to do and where to go. "If I look hard enough, I'll surely find some nuts and berries to take back to Granny," she thought.

So she set off, walking deeper and deeper into the woods. Hours later, she had only found a handful of raspberries. Soon it became too dark to hunt for more, but she didn't dare go home empty-handed. So she sat down on a log, shivering with cold and fright.

Suddenly, moving in a cloud of fog, a woman appeared. She was very small and thin. Like a shadow, she glided towards the little girl, her feet hardly touching the ground. In her wing-like arms, she carried a clay pot.

"Dear girl," the woman said, "I know you have had a hard life with barely enough to eat. I have brought you something. Take this good pot and treat it kindly. Whenever you are hungry, all you have to say is,

'Dear pot, cook for me. Give me tasty porridge,' and the pot will cook the porridge all by itself. When you have eaten your fill, say: 'Dear pot, now you must stop,' and the pot will stop cooking."

"Thank you, thank you!" whispered the little girl. Holding the pot tightly, she ran back to the house.

"Granny, look what I have! A good woman in the woods gave me this magic pot! Watch this: 'Dear pot, cook for me, give me tasty porridge!'"

Instantly the pot began to cook. The old woman could not believe her eyes as it soon bubbled with hot porridge. She and the little girl grabbed their spoons and ate until they couldn't eat anymore. Then the girl said the magic words, "Dear pot, now you must stop," and it did.

As time went by, the girl took very good care of the pot, never allowing herself or the mean old woman to overeat. She learned just how much and no more was needed for good healthy nourishment. She stored the pot safely on a high shelf and kept it clean, thinking how the woman in the woods had been so good to her.

But one day, when the girl was out picking berries, the mean old woman decided to fill herself up with as much porridge as her stomach could hold. She pulled the pot off the shelf, hung it over the fire and said, "Dear pot, cook for me. Give me tasty porridge!"

Immediately the pot started cooking. The woman looked at the bubbling mass, then sat down at her table, covered her front with a large napkin and ate and ate until her stomach was so full that she nearly burst. She got up to tell the pot to stop cooking, but she couldn't remember the magic words. The pot cooked on and on, bubbling higher and higher, rising over the rim and cascading down the sides. Still the pot kept cooking, until the house was full of porridge from floor to ceiling. It crushed against the windows and broke through the door. Then it flowed out into the garden and beyond.

When the little girl arrived back home and saw what was happening, she loudly gave the magic command: "Dear pot, now you must stop!" and so it did.

But the mean old woman had cooked up so much trouble that nothing could be done. The porridge had buried her along with the house and the garden. In their place was a mountain of porridge, which still stands there today. People say that whoever wants to find the magic pot must eat through the stale porridge mountain.

"Now what will I do?" the little girl cried. "I have no roof over my head and no food to eat."

"You will come with me."

The little girl looked up to see the good woman from the woods floating towards her. "Do not worry," she said kindly. "Because you took great care of my gift, you have shown how generous you are. Take my hand. You will never be hungry again."

The Fox and the Crab

(Lapsa un vēzis)

One day, a fox came upon a crab scurrying back and forth over the sand.

"Why do you run sideways?" the fox jeered. "Any fool knows that to get from one place to another, you have to go forwards."

"You think you're so smart, how about a race?" answered the crab.

"Ha!" laughed the fox. "Sure, I'll race you. Line up right here next to me."

And so, both took their stand side by side and designated the finish line. At the count of three, the crab clamped his claw onto the fox's bushy tail and held on tight as the fox charged forth like an arrow.

Having crossed the finish line, the crab let go of the fox's tail. The fox turned around, expecting to see the crab far behind him, but he was standing right there in front of him. "What took you so long?" the crab asked.

The fox scratched his head, realizing he had been defeated. "I guess you're much faster than I thought you were. You win," he said and slunk off into the woods.

And so the sideways-scurrying crab outsmarted the forward-dashing fox.

Treasures Buried in the Ground

(Zemē aprakti dārgumi)

O nce there was a father who lived with his three sons. When the father became old and close to death, he called his sons to his bedside.

"Dear boys, I feel that my days are numbered. During my long life I have not been able to save up any great wealth; therefore, I cannot leave you much in the way of an inheritance except the garden in front of the house. This garden always fed us because great riches are hidden in it. When I'm gone, you should dig up the garden carefully and then maybe you will find great treasures that will help you live without worry."

Exhausted from this long speech, the father passed away. After the funeral, the sons went to work. They dug the garden for many days and nights, rooting up every last foot and raking through all the soil, but they never found any treasure.

"Listen here," said the first son. "I think our father has pulled the wool over our eyes. There is no hidden treasure in this garden!"

"You're right," agreed the second brother. "We have wasted our time and strength for nothing."

"Why for nothing?" asked the third. "Look how tender and nice the soil is! It begs to be planted with fruit trees and vegetables."

The brothers agreed and began to plant. First, they hoed in seeds and vegetable roots, then berry bushes along the edges and fruit trees at the far end.

All summer long, the crops grew remarkably well, and in the fall the brothers gathered a rich harvest. And so it was the second, third, and all the years thereafter. What they did not need they sold in the market or gave to the poor.

By and by the brothers understood what treasures their dying father had spoken about. Faithfully they prepared the garden every spring and took in the harvest every fall. They lived well and without any worries about what they would eat and what they would wear. They learned that good crops grow from deep roots, that hard work puts bread on the table, and that honest people deserve the fruits of their labor. And they did not forget to pass on their father's wisdom to their own sons and daughters.

The Serpent's Bride

(Zalkša līgava)

One hot summer day, at high noon, three girls went to the sea for a swim. Splashing in the cool water, one said, "I wonder which one of us will be married first? When I get married, I'm going to wear my mother's dress and put flowers in my hair. All the neighbors will say how beautiful I am, and my groom will be the most handsome man in the village."

"I'm going to marry a nice boy with a good farm and plenty of cows," the second girl said. "I'll have six children, and I'll prepare the best meals for them and my husband. I'll live happily ever after tending to my family and farm."

But the third one said nothing. Floating on her back, Ziednese gazed at the clouds floating above her in the blue sky. She wondered what secrets they held in their silent silver beauty. Where did they come from, and where did they go? She thought about the mysteries of life all around her and about the silent spirits that seemed to coax her to dive deeper, pulling her away from the shore. Why wasn't she like her friends who wanted nothing more than a happy marriage? Why was she different?

"Uh, oh!" one suddenly called. "It's milking time! We have to get home!"

Awakened from her daydreaming, Ziede flipped over and swam like a fish to the shore. Back on the sand, she reached for her white linen blouse and stopped short: On the shirt lay a snake, glimmering like gold in the sunshine.

"What are you doing here?" she asked, surprised. "Please let me have my clothes or I will be late for milking."

"On one condition," said the snake. "You must promise to come back tomorrow."

"Why?" Ziede asked.

"Just promise me, and I'll leave you for now," the snake said.

"I promise," she answered, and the snake disappeared into the sea.

The next day, Ziede returned alone to the water, drawn by some inexplicable force that she couldn't resist. She waded into the sea, hoping the strange snake would appear. She felt a gentle nip on her toe and suddenly there he was, swimming around her, up and down, coaxing her further out to sea. Why was she so drawn to this strange creature?

"This is silly," she laughed. "I can't spend all day swimming. I have to get home."

Back on the sand, the snake was again lying on her blouse.

"Oh please, let me have my clothes! I have to get home," she pleaded, although she didn't really want to leave.

"Promise to come back tomorrow," the snake said, and Ziede agreed.

On her third visit to the sea, the snake again would not let her retrieve her blouse.

"Oh please, I don't want to go, but I have to get home for milking!"

"On one condition," said the snake, "you must promise to be my bride. Give me your ring to seal this vow, and I will let you go . . . for now." Ziede pulled the ring off her finger and gave it to the snake, who slid it right down his slick torso onto his tail and dove into the sea.

Three weeks passed, and Ziede thought only about this mysterious snake, dreaming of the day when he would come and take her as his bride. Day after day, she sat on the beach and waited. At last, he appeared. He rose out of the water with great pomp, sitting in a golden boat, a golden crown on his head and the ring on his tail. The harnesses glistened with diamonds, and a long procession of sea creatures accompanied him, playing their lutes and reeds and beating their drums. Ziede watched the procession in wonder, moving closer and closer to the water.

"Come with me to my kingdom in the sea," the snake called. Ziede waded into the water and got into the boat. The creatures covered her with a sheer, white veil and placed a myrtle wreath on her head. On the shore, her family, friends and neighbors sang a farewell song as they watched the boat disappear over the horizon.

"Dear serpent, I am so happy! I don't know why I was so drawn to you and the sea, but I know that I belong here. I do not want to be like other girls, just milking cows and washing clothes. I knew there was more to life, and you have rescued me from that fate." She embraced her husband with real love and kissed him. Suddenly, he shed his skin, and before her stood a prince in his royal robes.

"I am the Sea King, and you are my bride. Together we will rule these waves and all the wonders it holds," he said.

And so Ziede lived a long happy life, free of earthly worries in the castle under the waves.

The Wolf and the Raven

(Vilks un krauklis)

Once upon a time, a wolf, running through the woods, stepped upon a nail that pierced his foot. In terrible pain, he lay down, unable to walk and thinking he would die at any moment.

Seeing the wolf suffering, a raven flew down for a closer look. Suddenly, the wolf sat up and caught the bird in his mouth, ready to eat him up. At that, the quick-witted bird pleaded for his life: "Oh, my brother, I saw what happened to you and came to help. You can't swallow me! Who better than I to remove the nail from your paw?"

The wolf thought for a second and realized the raven was right. He let him go.

The raven hopped over to the wolf's injured paw and, with his strong beak, gripped the nail and pulled it out. The wolf groaned in relief.

"Thank you! From now on, I promise to share my food with you. You will never go hungry with me around."

And so both were very happy. The wolf's paw was healed, and the raven's life was saved. To this day, wolves and ravens work together to survive the cold winters.

Miracle Bread

(Brīnumklaips)

Once a father had a son who, in his sixth year, still hadn't learned to walk. He had no mother, and his father could not understand what was wrong with the boy. Day after day, arguments, scolding and anger filled this sad household.

"Get up!" the father would demand, kicking the leg of his son's bed. "If I had refused to walk, my father would have whipped me black and blue. I've never seen such a lazy child in all my life!"

Thinking he might embarrass his son into walking, the father went so far as to put him in a wagon and parade him around in front of the neighbors: "Look at my son. Six years old and he still hasn't taken the trouble to learn to walk!"

This humiliating experience only made the boy cry more. He simply refused to take even one step.

"You can go to bed without supper tonight. Maybe that will teach you a lesson."

Finally, at a complete loss, the father decided to ask for help. He loaded his son like a sack of potatoes into the wagon and went to see the neighboring farmer and his wife. This neighbor was a master — a *saimnieks* — who, with his wife — a *saimniece*—owned a large, well-managed estate. Both had a good reputation as being kind and wise people who had risen from humble peasant stock and, through hard, honest work, had been amply blessed by Mother Fortune.

They had many servants who worked in the fields, cared for the animals and helped with other never-ending jobs around the estate. It was past noon when the troubled father, pulling the wagon with his son lying in it, opened the gate and went to knock on the manor door. Both father and son were nervous, tired and hungry when the master opened the door and asked them to come in. The father, hat in hand, bowed and explained the reason for his visit.

"Ah, I see," the *saimnieks* said, looking closely at the boy. "Let's see what we can do about this."

The master went into the kitchen and came back with a round, freshly baked loaf of rye bread. He put it on the table, its tempting aroma filling the sunny room. The father reached out for the knife, but the host stopped him: "My friend, you are not allowed to cut into the loaf, but you, little boy, may help yourself. Just come over here, and you can have as much as you want. Or you can go hungry. It's up to you."

And hungry the little fellow was. Very hungry. As nobody lifted him out of the wagon, he cried, kicked and screamed, but the men simply sat at the end of the table, talking about crops, horses, and their neighbors. Red-faced and frustrated, the boy kicked harder and cried louder until he finally collapsed, exhausted and sniffling.

Hearing all this noise, the *saimniece* came through the door, wiping her hands and wondering what was going on.

"I'm sorry for this upset, ma'am," said the father. "No matter how much I scold and punish the boy, he just will not get up and walk. He is very stubborn."

The *saimniece* saw the problem in an instant: "Tell me, sir, when your ox refuses to plow the field, do you beat him? When your hen refuses to lay an egg, do you take away her feed?"

"Of course not!" the father laughed. He then quickly realized what the woman was getting at and became serious once again.

"A bit of kindness, patience, and understanding can go a long way," she said.

Looking gratefully at the woman, the boy's eyes again filled with tears. Then, to everyone's surprise, he put one leg over the edge of the wagon, glanced around and let the other leg follow. He stretched out his arms toward her, and she sat down and pulled him close to her.

Seeing the boy eye the loaf of bread, the *saimniece* gently spoke: "You must be hungry, dear one. Did you know that bread is the miracle that gives us life? It makes us strong and healthy, because it holds the power of the earth inside it. Yes, little boy, it is a gift from God, and people all over the world eat bread of all kinds. We depend mostly on our rye bread. You, too, must eat it so you can grow up strong and handsome. You are nice looking, you know, with such bright blue eyes and curly hair."

Warmed by such kind words, the boy shyly smiled at the woman. "Do you know how much work has gone into baking this small loaf?" she asked. The boy shook his head.

"Well, last fall, before the first frost, this man," she touched her husband's arm, "rose with the sun, harnessed his horses and went out to plough our large field. Then, with different machines, our servants and horses rolled and smoothed the furrows. After the soil settled, the master took a large, full basket of the finest seeds, strapped the basket over his shoulders, and walked back and forth over the field, in straight lines, scattering the seeds with even swings of his arm. He worked until sunset. When he finished his part, we all rested, watched and waited for the sun, wind, rain, and snow to do the rest.

"The seeds sprouted, turning the field green throughout the winter. They grew faster in spring and summer and into autumn. Then the field turned to gold and was ready to harvest.

"Our *saimnieks* took his scythe and went out to cut the rye — as tall as himself, the stalks bent, heavy with fat seeds. He followed his straight lines. Other men went behind him raking and binding armfuls for us women to gather and tie into sheaves. We went about this hard work

35

with singing, to lighten our labor. Yes, dear boy, it takes a lot of strength and patience to make a whole field stand upright, the sheaves leaning against each other so no wind can blow the stacks over and no rain can soak them through. And you know how hard it is to stand, bend, lift and carry heavy loads, don't you?"

The boy roused himself, "*Jā.*"

"If there is a good, hot dry spell, all is well," she went on, "and the sheaves can be gathered for thrashing, but God help us if it rains!"

"But it didn't rain," the boy quietly interjected, his face brightening.

"Not this year . . . and I remember how excited we were when the big, black threshing machine rolled into our yard! We had to be careful because it happened often enough that a man's finger or hand would get caught in the machine's sharp teeth. Yes, my uncle lost his index finger, and it never grew back! Anyway, it took us three full days to clear the fields and store the grain, and we were as glad to see the threshing machine go as when it came. The hardest part was finished. The sacks of seeds, when dry, were driven to the mill and ground into flour. The straw was used for bedding the stables. Nothing was wasted.

"We were ready to celebrate, eat and be merry, and then we had our day of rest. Dear boy, this work goes on from year to year, season to season."

Tired from the long day and comforted by the woman's sweet voice, the boy's eyes started growing heavy, and his head drooped against the woman's heart.

"Then I have to do the baking, which takes two days," she continued. "I scrape the large bread trough clean, then mix in cool water, a blob of old dough, a large slice of rye bread, sugar, flour, and kefir. Then I cover it and let it rise. The next morning I add boiling and warm water, more flour, caraway seeds, more sugar, salt and other secret ingredients. I let the dough rise for six hours, and then I knead until my sticky hands are clean. At last I place the loaves on the baking board, mark each with a cross, cover them with maple leaves and push the heavy load into the hot oven. It bakes there for six more hours and comes out dark, shiny, and delicious."

Now lulled into a deep sleep, the little boy saw himself jumping up and trying to grab the loaf. But it moved away from him, slowly at first. Then it rolled on, faster and faster — out the door, across the yard, down the cartroad, over the meadow, and up the footbridge. There it stopped. It seemed to wink and laugh, daring the boy to catch it. But just when the bread was almost in his grasp, *whirrlll . . .* it spun around like a top and fell into the river. The boy cried out and woke up with a start, brushing the sleep from his eyes. Confused, he looked around and saw his father, the *saimnieks,* and the *saimniece* smiling at him.

"Come to the table, my dear," the master said, while his wife spread butter and honey on a thick slice of bread for the boy. She then lovingly helped him to stand up.

Everyone watched as the boy took one step, then another and another. Now standing tall and proud, his father nearly wept with joy.

On the way home, pulling his wagon full of good things to eat, the boy asked: "Father, is bread a miracle?"

"Son, I never thought of it that way, but yes, I believe it is."

The boy said nothing and, leaving his wagon, he ran over the meadow and hill to the footbridge. He looked down into the still water and saw the reflection of a proud young man smiling back at him among the ripples and clouds.

How a Peasant Wrote a Complaint to the King

(Kā zemnieks rakstīja sūdzību ķēniņam)

A long, long time ago, a peasant's potato field was dug up by pigs belonging to the noble lord of a manor. The peasant was so upset that he decided to write a complaint to the king himself. But he did not know how to write, so he had to come up with another way to voice his concerns.

He went out to his favorite spot, pulled a piece of bark from a birch tree, and sat down on a log. He took a piece of charcoal out of his pocket and drew some very small dots, then larger dots, then even larger oblong dots on the bark.

At this time, the king happened to be out on his daily walk and saw the peasant hard at work. "What are you doing?" he asked.

"I'm writing a book of complaints to the king," the peasant answered.

The king looked closely, but saw no words – only a bunch of dots from end to end. "What do all these signs mean?" he asked. The peasant, a bit irritated at the interruption, explained: "These dots are the lord's piglets. The bigger ones are the lord's pigs, and these tiny dots are my potatoes, which the lord's pigs have dug up. Now you can see for yourself the loss I am suffering. That's why I'm going to take this book of complaints all the way to the king."

Seeing that the peasant did not recognize him, the king encouraged him: "Go ahead! We all know how good and just our king is! He will help you."

"Really? You think so?"

"Yes, to be sure. And good luck!"

Early the next morning, the peasant dressed in his Sunday best and went up to the castle, but the guards would not let him through. The king, watching from his balcony, called down and ordered the guards to open the gate. Then he hurried inside, put on his wig and crown, wrapped his crimson cape over his shoulders, and sat upon his throne.

Minutes later, the peasant entered the hall. Clutching the strip of bark to his heart, he bowed all the way to the ground. He then turned to the page and gave him his book of complaints to take up to the throne. The king asked the page to read it, but of course he could not. Pretending to be irritated, the king said, "Give it to me. I bet I can read it." The page handed him the strip of bark.

"You see, it is written here, plain as day: These tiny little dots are the peasant's potatoes. The bigger ones are the lord's piglets, and these very big ones, they are the lord's pigs. The lord's pigs with their piglets have dug up the potatoes."

The page's mouth dropped open in surprise, and the peasant smiled in gratitude.

Turning to his guest, the king promised that he would correct the situation and write a proclamation to all the landlords of his kingdom, instructing them to treat the peasants with respect: "Dear man, this cannot be tolerated. I will order your lord to pay you fairly for all the damage and grief you have suffered."

The page and other members of the court were amazed. To read such hieroglyphics, their king must indeed be the smartest man in the kingdom. They could not stop talking about this and, before the day was over, all the neighbors knew what had happened. The story, naturally, traveled like the wind, and soon the folk honored their king and called the peasant a hero, even making up proverbs in his honor: *A clever mind does clever things. The eye can see far, but the mind sees farther. Not my field and not my pig!* Many of these sayings are still remembered to this day.

Then all the lords admired and feared their king as never before and kept their pigs out of the peasants' fields. The people prospered, as they lived together in peace, respecting each other's property, rights, and potatoes.

Fortune Fulfills Three Wishes

(Laima izpilda trīs vēlēšanās)

On a winter evening, Laima (Mother Fortune), in her walks around the world, came to a lonely hut and asked permission to come inside and warm herself. The man and his wife welcomed her in, so when she was ready to leave, she said: "Because you have been kind to me, I shall grant you three wishes."

"I wish that a link of sausage would be frying in my pan!" the wife exclaimed. And the next moment, a sausage appeared on the stove, splattering away. The man rushed up to the stove and angrily scolded his wife, "You fool! I wish that link of sausage would get stuck to your nose! Why didn't you wish for money or something valuable?"

Suddenly, the link of sausage flew out of the pan and attached itself to the tip of the wife's nose. No matter how hard they tried, they could not pull it off. The man begged Laima to remove the link, and she satisfied his wish.

As she walked out the door, Mother Fortune turned back to the couple and said: "You are not the first ones who carelessly squandered my gifts and your chances. You were granted three wishes, and three wishes you received. Good bye."

The Proud Fly

(Iedomīgā muša)

Once there lived a proud fly who was larger than all the other flies. One day she decided that being a fly was simply not enough for her.

"I want to become a wasp," she naughtily announced to her fellow flies and began knitting herself a black-and-yellow wasp skirt. When she was done, she put it on, buttoned it up, and flew to the garden where the wasps lived.

"Who are you?" the wasps asked.

"I am a fly, but I want to be a wasp," she answered.

"Some wasp you'd be," they buzzed. "Where's your stinger? You can't be a wasp if you don't have a stinger."

Undeterred, the fly flew home and knitted herself a cuckoo skirt. She put it on and flew to the meadow where the cuckoos lived.

"Who are you?" they asked.

"I am a fly, but I want to be a cuckoo," she answered.

"Some cuckoo you'd be!" they clucked. "Where are your feathers? You can't be a cuckoo if you don't have any feathers."

So the fly flew back home and decided she wanted to be an eagle. She knitted herself an eagle skirt, put it on, and flew to where the eagles lived.

"Who are you?" they asked.

"I am a fly, but I want to be an eagle," she answered.

"You can't be an eagle!" they squawked. "All eagles have a braid down their backs, but you don't have one."

"Okay, fine. I guess I'll go back to the cuckoos," she reluctantly said, her pride starting to fade. She quickly undid the top button, took off her eagle skirt, and flew back to the cuckoos.

"I want to be a cuckoo after all, and I want to stay with you," she said.

"You can stay with us, if that is what you want to do," they answered. "But winter is coming, and we'll soon be flying to warmer lands."

"Oh," the fly sadly said. "I can't fly that far. I'm going to go back to the wasps."

She undid the top button, took off her cuckoo skirt, and flew back to the wasps in her yellow-and-black striped skirt.

"I'm back, and I want to stay with you," she announced.

"All right. Stay on, if that's what you want to do, but our nest is very narrow. You won't like that."

The fly crawled into the nest anyway, determined to fit in with her new friends. But oh, what a racket! Never had there been such buzzing and stinging! The poor fly got more than a funny tickle. She barely escaped the nest alive.

Outside in the sunshine, she reconsidered her foolish ambitions: "I am a fly and nothing more. Only a fly, and a fly I must remain for the rest of my life." She unbuttoned the top button, took off the wasp skirt she had so carefully knitted and let it drop. Then, wearing only her drab fly dress, she flew back home.

"So you've returned," her sister coldly said.

"Yes, I guess I just have to accept that I'm nothing but a lowly fly," she sadly answered. "I don't have a stinger, feathers, or a braid. I'm nothing special."

"What do you mean?" her sister asked. "It's true you don't have those things, but you have your own gifts. What about all those beautiful eyes of yours? You can see above, below, in front and behind all at once! And what about your long, thin legs? You can hop and dance better than any creature in the forest. And your wings! You can fly like a comet, so fast no one even sees you! It's fine to aspire to great things, but you must first be happy with what you have."

After hearing these wise words, the proud fly realized that she truly was special and didn't need to change. "You're right, sister," she admitted. "I can't be something I'm not."

So the proud fly made peace with the other flies, and they all got to work, preparing their nest for the coming winter. When it was finished, they gathered inside, settled down, and went to sleep. Perhaps they are still sleeping – unless some wasp, cuckoo, or eagle had awakened them to a new spring.

Maia and Paia
(Īstā meita un pameita)

Once upon a time, a mother had two daughters: a stepdaughter, whose name was Maia, and a biological daughter, whose name was Paia. Maia was pretty and kind, but Paia was scowling and mean. She had become lazy and often lost her temper. She was also very jealous of Maia.

One day, Maia went to draw water from the well when something unusual happened. As she looked down, she saw two little men, seemingly dancing and prancing on the water. She watched them in wonder for some time. Then she picked two apples from a tree and threw them into the well. Each of the men caught one, looked up, and saw Maia smiling at them. "How can we reward you, pretty girl?" they called. "Thank you, but I don't need any reward," she said and drew up the brimming pail and went back to the house.

As soon as she stepped inside, Paia exclaimed, "What gold you have in your hair! How did that happen?"

Surprised, Maia loosened her braids and looked. Sure enough, her hair was like spun gold! "I guess the two little men in the well gave it to me," she said. "I suppose that whenever anyone throws apples to them, they repay that person with golden hair."

Hearing that, the stepmother told Paia to go to the well so that her hair too would turn to gold. The girl ran to the well and leaned over. She also saw the two little men dancing about, but instead of apples, Paia picked up two stones and laughingly threw them down, hitting the men right on their heads.

"What are you doing up there? You almost knocked our heads off!" shouted one of the men, as angry as could be. "You will be punished for this!"

Paia did not listen to their curses and ran straight back to the house. As soon as she opened the door, her mother cried out, "Oh, my precious, your sister must have lied to us! You don't have golden hair but an owl's tail hanging from your forehead!"

The girl looked in the mirror and, to her horror, she saw that her mother was right. From then on, both the mother and her daughter hated Maia for her golden hair, thinking she had played some sort of trick on them. "From now on, you can do all the chores by yourself!" the stepmother said.

As time passed, word of a girl with hair like spun gold spread through the kingdom, eventually reaching the ear of a nobleman. He immediately called to his servant: "Order the coachman to fetch her. If she is as beautiful as you say, I will marry her!"

As ordered, the coachman drove to the farmhouse and was greeted by the stepmother. "My master has ordered me to bring the girl with the golden hair to his manor!" But the stepmother refused to obey: "I'll let the one go if you take her sister also." She argued stubbornly until the coachman could do nothing but hold the door open for both girls to step into the coach.

On the road, Maia complained, "I don't know what's the matter with me, but my head hurts badly."

"Don't worry," said Paia. "When we cross the bridge over the river, open the door, lean out, and close your eyes. Then Water Mother will come up and cure your headache."

The trusting girl did as advised and leaned out as far as she dared. Then Paia quickly stood up and pushed her out the door. She fell into the river, while the coach rolled on, leaving her behind. All this happened so quickly and quietly that the coachman noticed nothing until they reached the manor. When he got down and opened the door, he discovered that, instead of two girls, he had brought only one. Confused, he trembled in fear of what his master would do to him.

The nobleman, anxious to see the golden-haired beauty, rushed to meet her, but when he saw only the girl with an owl's tail hanging down her face, grinning shamelessly at him, he was so furious that he lost all reason: "Lock her up in the dungeon!"

The next day, the master's cook heard a sound coming from the chimney. He poked his head in and saw a golden duckling flying around inside, trying to get free. He didn't want to get dirty with soot, so he stuck a mop handle up to the bird and brought her out. "What a beautiful little duck! Her feathers shine like pure gold. I need to show her to my master. This is surely a good omen."

When the nobleman saw the golden duck, he grabbed her from the cook and started stroking and petting her. He could not keep his hands off the golden feathers. But the duckling wriggled out of his arms and flew away. As if awakened from a dream, the master chased her down and caught her by the leg before she could fly out the window. Now he held her so tightly that she nearly choked. He did not let up and squeezed still harder and then, suddenly, there in front of him stood the beautiful girl with the golden hair. After the master came out of shock, she told him all that had happened to her – all that Paia, the Owltail, and her stepmother had done to her.

"But how did you turn into a duck?" asked the nobleman.

"It was a miracle!" Maia answered. "When I fell into the river, I almost drowned. I tried to swim, but the rapids were too strong. Suddenly I felt the arms of Water Mother around me, bringing me back to the surface. Then she turned me into a golden duck so I could swim to shore and fly to you. Unfortunately, I landed on the roof and fell into the chimney."

Having heard the whole story, the master called up Owltail from the dungeon and, pretending to seek her advice, asked, "Listen, clever girl, perhaps you could tell me how to punish someone who would nearly drown another person?" Without thinking, Owltail answered: "Such a person should be tied to a team of horses and dragged through the streets!" "All right," the master said. "You have chosen your own punishment. It will happen tomorrow morning as you have spoken." And so it did.

Once the horrors were past, the nobleman asked for Maia's hand in marriage. The golden-haired orphan answered, "On one condition. You must promise not to ruffle my feathers like you did when I was a duck. If you are rough with me, I will only fly away." "Agreed!" the nobleman vowed, and the two lived happily together for a long time.

A Rabbit Goes into the World

(Zaķis dodas pasaulē)

Once a rabbit became bored with living in thickets and hiding underground, so he made himself a little red wagon, harnessed himself, and rode away, hoping to find some new friends. The first thing he found on his way was a darning needle.

"Where are you going?" he asked. "Why don't you climb into my wagon and let's go on together?"

"All right," the darning needle answered, climbed into the wagon, and the two rode on.

After a while, they met a pin. The rabbit invited the pin to get into the wagon, and they continued on their journey. In like manner, the rabbit addressed a sewing needle, a smoldering piece of coal, a rock, and last of all, a duck.

All excited, the rabbit pulled the wagon at high speed, zigging and zagging until he stopped suddenly at a strange hut at the edge of the woods. The door was hidden inside a mesh of piled up branches and vines to confuse anyone who tried to enter, but enter they did.

The place was empty, and so they made themselves as comfortable as they pleased. The duck jumped into a barrel of water that stood near the door; the darning needle stuck itself into the bedspread; the sewing needle chose a pillow; the pin, a towel; the rock perched over the doorway; and the coal fell into an easy chair.

After it turned dark, the master of the hut passed the small, sooty window and opened the door, giving the rabbit a start, for he recognized him as a well-known criminal, with whom he had had serious dealings. But the criminal, suspecting nothing, stopped as he usually did at the barrel of water to wash his hands. That awoke the duck, who had been quietly floating round and round, her head tucked under a wing.

Suddenly frightened, she rose up and started beating and splashing, making a tempest in the barrel and blinding the man. He grabbed his towel, but the pin pricked his face, making it bleed. He plopped down in his chair, but the coal burned his behind. Crying out in pain, he fell backwards onto his bed, where the needles stuck into his back. Twisting, turning, and bleeding, he finally pulled the needles out. As he ran out the door, the rock over the doorway lost its balance, fell, and hit him on the head. Cursing and yelling in agony, the man fled into the night.

The criminal was never seen again, but the rabbit and his companions settled down and lived happily together in the little hut by the woods.

The Magic Horse

(Brīnuma zirgs)

Once there lived a young man who worked as an apprentice for a blacksmith. The fellow's job was to make screws. So that's what he did. He made screws of all types and all sizes. He always saved one of each for himself and brought it home. After some time, he had a sack full of the most usual and unusual screws.

The apprentice kept the sack in his little room, and in the evenings, he tinkered with them, screwing them together in different ways to see what he could make. Then, to his surprise, and quite by chance, he made himself a horse. It turned out to be the kind of horse that rides in the air, which was fine with the fellow. All he had to figure out was how to control this screwy horse! So, he fixed it up in such a way that one screw would make it go up, the other come down.

Because this was quite an amazing innovation, the fellow decided to make some money by showing the horse around town. The people were amazed, and the apprentice collected a good sum.

Now able to buy decent clothes, he decided to go to the king and show him his handiwork. And that is what he did. The old king was a bit skeptical, but the prince was very impressed and begged the apprentice to allow him to take the horse for a ride.

"All right, but be careful and pay attention to what screws turn which way," he warned. "Don't worry, your majesty," said the fellow to the king. "I'll demonstrate how my steed is put together and how it works."

Very carefully and slowly, the fellow showed the prince the function of every screw and told him to be sure to remember which screw made the horse go up, which down.

"Yes, yes," the prince said, in a great hurry to fly off. "Don't worry, I'll remember!"

"All right," said the fellow and helped the prince mount the mechanical horse.

In no time they were riding high over the fields. After an hour or so, the prince was ready to come down, but he could not remember which screw to turn. He tried the DOWN screw, but the horse went UP. And he kept going higher and higher and farther and farther until the prince couldn't even see the land below. Without knowing it, he had crossed the border and, after nights and days of flying, he found himself in another kingdom, where the mountains were very high. "I can land here," he thought.

He tried another screw, and luckily it was the right one. The prince slowly dropped back down to the ground, but he was now in a strange land, a strange kingdom, and a strange town. He didn't want anyone to steal the horse, so he took it apart like the apprentice had shown him and put all the screws in a sack. He did not realize that he was in the capital city, where the king lived in his castle on top of the highest mountain.

Soon the displaced prince learned that the king was proud and mean. He had a daughter whom he had locked away in a high tower so that no one could get to her. At first the prince paid no attention to the stories, but then, one day, as he walked through the woods, he saw a strangely built tall and round house – a tower of sorts – with one window at the top and no doors. When he inquired what kind of a building that was, he was told it was the tower where the princess was imprisoned.

This, of course, aroused the young man's curiosity. He wanted to see her. And so, that same evening he carefully took the screws out of the sack and reassembled the horse. He was surprised by how easily the parts went together, as if someone where guiding his hands. Before the moon had risen, he mounted the horse and took off, up into the air and towards the tower.

He flew over the sleeping houses and castle, across the tops of trees, over the hills and mountains, in and out of low-lying clouds, until he came to the tower. Then, very carefully, he turned a special screw, and the horse took him to the princess's window, which was large enough for him and his horse to go through.

Surprised, the princess cried out. She was so happy to see another person that she ran right into the charming prince's arms. When they finally stepped back and looked at each other, they liked what they saw: She was lovely, and he was handsome, though quite wind-blown.

The two stayed up all night talking. The princess described her lonely days in the tower, and the prince told her about his far-away homeland. As the sun started to rise, the prince said he must be going.

"Promise me you will come back tomorrow!" the princess pleaded.

"I promise," the prince replied, and he mounted his horse, went out the window and back to town. He slept in a hay barn and returned to the tower the next night and the next.

Meanwhile, the king's sleepy guards rubbed their eyes, guessing that something unusual was going on up in the tower and went to tell the king: "Your majesty, we believe that someone is in the tower with the princess. Three nights in a row we have heard laughing and singing, when before we only heard weeping and moaning."

"How could that be?" shouted the king. "Haven't you been watching her? And how could anyone get to her when there is no door or stairway?"

"That's just it," said one of the braver guards. "It's all so strange. There are no footprints on the ground, no marks, ropes, or hair on the wall – nothing. Yet, as we stood guard below, we heard voices coming through the open window. And they were happy voices, which we don't often hear in this kingdom."

"A trap must be built," said the angry king, "and it must be hung outside the window. Right now! Stop staring and get on with it!"

"Yes, your majesty."

That same day, the king's construction crew built a trap large enough to catch a man. They mounted it outside the window, while the princess watched from a dark corner.

That night, when the prince rode up to the window, he saw the trap. He very carefully guided his horse through it and the window, but his jacket snagged on the wires. When he pulled the jacket out, he didn't notice that a piece had torn off and was left hanging in the trap. As the sun rose, the prince again mounted his horse, went out the window, through the trap and back to town.

In the morning, the king went to see what was going on. He ordered the trap be brought down. Then he saw the scrap of cloth caught in the trap. "Now find the rest of that jacket!" he ordered. "And bring me the person wearing it. Justice will be done!"

The servants obeyed. They scoured the land, found the prince and took him to the palace. They also brought down the princess, and both were thrown into the dungeon. The next day there was a trial of sorts. The pair was found guilty of treason and sentenced to be hanged. The scaffolds were prepared.

On the set day, both prisoners climbed the steps where two nooses were dangling. "Do you, young man, have a last wish?" asked the magistrate.

"I wish, if you please," said the prince bravely, "to check a few screws in this scaffold. I want to make sure it is up to code."

"What a ridiculous wish!" shouted the magistrate. "Are you making fun of us or what?"

"Oh, no," replied the prince, "I just have a strange need to tighten screws, and I would not be comfortable dangling there if even one screw were loose. I worry about the princess," he said giving her an assuring wink.

"All right. Your wish is granted," said the magistrate. The prince started turning the screws, one after another, quickly, precisely. And – presto! – he had created another flying horse!

While everyone stood gawking, the prince mounted his horse, pulled the princess up onto the saddle, and away they flew! Moments later the angry faces that had glared up at them were nothing but dots on the ground, and the houses and castle looked like children's building blocks.

"How things change, depending upon where you are!" said the princess. "We are free as the birds!"

"And happy!"

They kissed each other and flew off into the future, leaving the sad kingdom behind forever.

A Farmer's Bad Luck

(Pušelnieka nelaime)

Once there lived two farmers: one was rich, the other poor. The poor one struggled as much as he was able, but, no matter what, he could not get ahead.

One rainy evening, he sat at his table and sadly pondered why he was so unlucky. Suddenly, he heard a cheerful tune coming from behind his large clay oven. Forgetting his troubles, the poor man started to dance and jump around.

"Oh, my," he thought, "I don't even want to dance, but my feet do! Who is playing that song? Who are you? Come out and let me see you!"

From behind the oven came a tall, hollow man, dancing and playing a flute. The farmer grabbed hold of him and shook him by the neck: "Be still, you madman, and tell me who you are!"

"I am your bad luck – or more precisely, your misfortune, as they say in educated circles."

"Aha, so you are the reason for all my troubles! At last I have you, and I know what to do with you!"

The farmer squeezed his misfortune so tightly that it could not shake itself loose and put it into a sack. Then he climbed up a mountain, buried the sack at the top, and returned home.

From then on, the farmer's crops grew well, even on stony ground, and good fortune began to smile on him. People all around heard and saw the once-poor man singing and dancing and wondered what had happened.

The farmer's rich neighbor saw him also, but do you suppose he was happy for the poor man? Not he! Instead he envied his neighbor's success and was tormented by jealousy day and night. "I have to do something about this," he said to himself as he tossed and turned in his feather bed, which was much too soft.

The next day, the rich farmer walked over to his neighbor and said, nice as could be, "Tell me, brother, how did you get so rich so fast?"

"I buried my misfortune at the top of the mountain," said the happy man, smiling and whistling. "That's all."

"Aha!" said the other, very irritated. Having discovered this secret, he could not get out the door fast enough. He quickly headed up the mountain, found the grave where the farmer's misfortune lay "in peace," and dug it up.

Half asleep, the gaunt, skeleton of a man rubbed his eyes and asked, "Why did you wake me?"

"So you can go back to our friend, the poor farmer, who has become very rich while you slept. I suspect he misses you," the rich man answered.

Misfortune shook the dust off and became very jovial, hugging the rich man and saying, "Thank you, thank you for rescuing me!" He started dancing and whistling, and suddenly he put his arms around the up-to-now fortunate man's neck. Dust, dirt, and ashes flew all around, while misfortune laughed, "Why should I go to another," he asked with a sneer, hugging the man tightly and kissing his sweating cheeks and forehead, "when you're the one who sought me out and dug me up? I'll cling to you forever!"

This frightened the rich man out of his wits: "What are you talking about? Are you crazy?" And he tried to shake his new-found misfortune from him, but he could not. Instead it stuck closer than a shadow for the rest of his days.

A Cat and a Mouse

(Kaķis un pele)

Once upon a time, long ago, a cat and a mouse lived happily as a married couple. They shared a house and all the chores that entailed. The cat went out hunting, and the mouse prepared the food.

Since they were getting on in years, they decided they should start saving for old age or the day of hunger. They discussed what they should lay aside and decided that fat would be best, for it would keep well. So, the mouse started saving a little fat from each meal and soon had filled a good-sized clay pot. She sealed it with a maple leaf, and the two carried it to the woods, where they dug a hole in a thicket. They buried the pot, returned home, and life went on as before: He hunted; she cooked.

Inevitably, winter came. The cat could not find any food out in the fields, and it was not long before the pantry was empty. Nothing was left except some wheat crackers, which was fine for the mouse, but the cat craved meat and fat. As his stomach growled, he thought and thought about what to do. Then he remembered the pot they had hidden in the thicket. He looked at the mouse with his hungry, slanted eyes and said, "Listen here, I just realized! I have to go to my friend's son's christening. Let me have one cracker as is customary to bring."

The mouse thought nothing of this and gave him what he asked. The cat then took a roundabout way to the thicket and to the pot of fat. He dug it up, removed the maple leaf, smeared some fat onto the cracker, and ate his fill. He came back home at midnight where his wife was waiting up for him: "How was it? What did they name the little one?"

"Appetizer," the cat purred.

The next day, life went on as usual. The mouse nibbled at whatever she could find, while the cat lay about in a bad mood, hunger nudging at his ribs nonstop. "Oh, no!" the cat said, stretching. "I almost forgot. My other friend is also having his son christened. I promised to go. Could I please have another cracker?"

"Sure," said the trusting little mouse. Again, the cat went to the pot of fat and, in his sneaky, roundabout way, ate his fill. Then, upon his return at midnight, his sleepy wife asked him how it all went and what the name of the child was.

"Entrée," he yawned. To avoid further talking, he jumped on top of the warm oven and went to sleep.

Time passed, and winter held the fields in its grip. The cat's stomach growled, and the pot called him louder and louder. On one particularly cold day, he jumped off the stovetop and said to his hungry little wife, "I've got to go! There is another christening, and I've been invited. Another cracker, please."

The good mouse hesitated but did as asked, and the cat went on the same crooked path – straight to the fat. This time he finished it down to the bottom and licked the inside clean. Back home, the mouse asked again: "What is the baby's name?"

"Dessert," the cat half-purred, half-hissed and then he jumped on top of the oven, where it was nice and warm. Curling himself into a ball, he went to sleep. The weather had become much colder, and his paws were freezing.

The pair waited for spring, but winter would not let up. All the little creatures had hidden themselves in their holes and burrows. The cat told himself he couldn't catch any food even if he tried. Days passed. There was no scrap of meat nor crumb of bread to be found, not even in dark corners or behind the stove. Both cat and mouse despairingly wondered what to do.

Then the mouse remembered the pot of fat they had stored for just such bad times as these, "What's the use of starving to death, my poor old kitty cat? We are not as badly off as you think! Remember, we still have that pot of fat we hid in the thicket. Let's go and fill up on that. That will carry us over to springtime."

They went to the woods, the cat acting as if he had done nothing wrong. He dug up the pot. As he peered inside, running his tongue along the rim, he feigned surprise. "It's empty!" he exclaimed. "Oh no! What happened to our fat? Who ate it? Who would have known about it, sealed and buried as it was?"

Then the mouse scratched behind her ear, thinking. She remembered the sudden and frequent christenings and the strange names of all those godchildren, the crackers, the cat's coming home late, and his sound sleeping afterwards. Realizing he had been lying to her, she started to cry: "Oh, my husband, how you have cheated me! How could you? You never went to any christenings but to these woods to fill up on what belonged to both of us! You are a thief and a liar, and you don't care about me at all!"

At that the cat bared his claws, glared and hissed. The mouse rose up on her hind legs. They stood facing each other, eye to eye, tooth to tooth.

"It's none of your business what I do and where I go," the cat spewed. "You're right. I don't care, and yes, I did eat all the fat, and now I'll eat you too!"

The cat got ready to pounce upon the poor starved mouse. But, in the nick of time, she scurried down a deep, narrow hole under the root of a large fir tree. The cat went after her, but not even his paw would fit into the hiding place. "You couldn't fill me up anyway, you stringy little rodent," he sneered and slunk away.

And so, this marked the beginning of the permanent animosity between cats and mice. To this day, mice always run from cats, and cats always chase mice.

The Bear and the Hunter

(Lācis un mednieks)

Walking through the forest one day, a hunter came upon a hollow tree, its branches reaching to the sky. As an experienced stalker, he knew that some animal had been living in the hollow trunk because the ground around the tree's base was all scratched up.

"I'm going to see if I can catch something to bring home for supper," the hunter said.

He slowly climbed quite high up the tree to a hole in the hollow trunk. But as he peered inside, he lost his balance and fell headfirst, down to the bottom. Realizing he was stuck inside the tree, he made himself comfortable and waited for his last hour, thinking how upset his wife would be when he didn't return.

Finally, toward evening, he heard something climbing up the trunk. Judging from the sound of its claws scraping the wood, the hunter knew it was a bear, and he braced himself for the worst.

Once he reached the hole at the top of the tree, the bear turned around, went backwards through the hole, and slid all the way down to the bottom.

Realizing he had nothing to lose, the hunter grabbed hold of the bear's tail and pulled as hard as he could. As if struck by lightning, the bear bounced back up the hollow trunk like a rubber ball, dragging the hunter with him. Without even a glance, the bear jumped through the hole and down to the ground. The hunter let go of the bear's tail and watched him scamper away into the forest.

Then, whistling a happy tune, the hunter hurried home for his supper, "My wife is never going to believe this!"

The Garden Snake

(Zaltis)

Back in the old days, garden snakes lived together with people in their houses or huts, especially those close to low, swampy areas near woods and ponds. In one such house lived a farmer, his wife, and their newborn baby. In this house there also lived a garden snake. Because she kept the home free of mice and bugs, the snake was treated like a member of the family. She ate from the same bowl and slept in the same bed as the baby, and so the family got along peacefully.

Then it came time for the snake to lay her eggs. She needed to find a dry, dark place. And so, after much thought, she decided to make her nest in the baby's crib. Burrowing deep into the straw, she laid three eggs: "Here my babies will be kept safe and warm."

But the farmer's wife did not know the snake had hidden her eggs in the baby's crib. She had been going about her day as usual and decided, quite by accident, that it was time to change the straw in the baby's mattress. She took the mattress outside, opened it up, and dumped out the old straw and the snake's eggs along with it. Then she replaced the old straw with new and put the mattress back.

The snake had been out patrolling the garden for rodents, and she watched in horror as her eggs were thrown out with the old straw. Then she became angry, "How could she just throw my babies away? I'll show her!"

The snake then slithered inside, up the kitchen wall, and onto the stove where the farmer's wife kept the baby's milk in a jar, warm and ready for feeding time. The snake lifted her head up into the jar and squirted some venom into the milk: "If I have lost my babies, it is only fair that she lose hers." Then the snake waited to see what would happen.

The farmer's wife, not knowing she was being watched, continued her daily chores. She stepped out into the garden and, seeing the straw from the baby's bed, she decided to spread a little around her flowers to protect them from the morning frost. She picked up a handful of straw and then saw the snake's eggs.

"Oh no! Our little snake must have laid these in baby's bed. I better put them back."

She carefully carried the eggs into the house and to the baby's crib. She made a little nest in the straw and gently placed the eggs inside.

"I'm sorry, little snake," she said. "Your eggs are back where they belong, safe and sound. Now it's time to feed the baby."

The snake, realizing the farmer's wife had not meant to throw away her eggs, instantly regretted squirting venom into the baby's milk: "What should I do? I can't let her give the baby poisoned milk!" So, with a flick of her tail, the snake knocked over the jar of milk, spilling it down the sides of the stove and onto the floor.

"What has happened here?" the farmer's wife said, seeing the mess. "Surely this was just an accident. Don't worry, dear little snake. I have more milk."

And so the baby and the snake's eggs were both saved that day. In the spring, the family welcomed the three newborn snakes into the family, and the little household was very happy indeed.

The Wolf and the Horse

(Vilks un zirgs)

Once a very hungry wolf, slinking about the fields, saw a mare and a colt quietly grazing on red clover. The wolf walked up to the old mare and said, "Oh, how I love horses! Allow me to pet and kiss your beautiful colt. He seems very sweet."

"Oh, my dear wolf," the mare answered, "now that you're here, would you please take a look of my right leg? I don't know what happened, but I can't walk without limping."

The wolf could not believe what he heard. "This old mare must be very foolish," he thought. "First I'll eat her and then the colt."

And so the wolf leaned forward, pretending to examine the mare's leg. Suddenly, he got such a kick that he flew halfway across the field.

"Take that!" said the mare. "Do you think we horses are so gullible?"

And so the mother and son galloped safely away, laughing and whinnying into the distance.

Humiliated, the wolf pulled himself up and dragged himself back to the woods: "From now on, I'm sticking to rabbits."

Little Three-Span

(Sprīdītis)

There once lived a young man who stood only three full spans, so his father named him Sprīdītis. Although he was smaller than a garden gnome, he was braver than a giant. He often said, "If a little guy like me were not brave, he would not survive."

One day he decided to go out and see the world, which was very brave for a man who was smaller than a cat. He walked and walked until he came to a deep, dark forest. He was tired from his journey and decided to lie down and have a good rest.

He stretched himself out in a bed of moss and closed his eyes. At the same time, the lord of the land was out hunting in the forest and nearly stumbled over Sprīdītis: "Hey frog legs, get up! Who are you and why are you sleeping in my forest? Even a rabbit could run you down."

But Sprīdītis did not wake up. He just kept snoring. The lord told his fellow hunters to shoot into the air, which they did. One loud blast should have been enough to scare Sprīdītis to his feet, but he only moved his little finger and went on sleeping. The lord ordered another salvo. Sprīdītis moved one foot but still did not open his eyes. The lord ordered a third blast. Finally Sprīdītis awoke. He jumped up, mad as could be: "Why are you disturbing me? I'll slug you so hard you won't know which end is up!"

The lord, seeing such a brave elf for the first time in his life, started laughing and could not stop, bending over and holding his stomach: "You little shrimp! I bet you couldn't even smash a cricket!"

"Don't bother me with crickets," Sprīdītis shot back. "Let's talk about bears and not *what* bear but *how many*! And if you don't believe me, then just get me a bear and you'll see what I can do! You'll be so impressed – you'll even want me for a son-in-law."

"Ha ha! Listen, little braggart, if you can conquer a bear, I will promise you my daughter, but if you can't, you're the one who will get a beating."

The lord led Sprīdītis to a bear's den: "Let's see what you can do."

Sprīdītis picked up some pebbles, put them in his pocket and went into the den where the bear was sleeping. He took one pebble, threw it with all his might, and hit the bear on the head. The bear woke up, dazed and wondering who dared to stir him from his slumber. Sprīdītis threw another pebble and hit the bear again. The bear growled. Sprīdītis threw another pebble and hit the poor bear a third time. Furious now, the bear stood up on his back legs, roared and charged after our hero.

Sprīdītis ran as fast as a rabbit – straight into the king's barn – with the bear hot on his heels. But as soon as Sprīdītis scampered through the doorway, he – smack! – dropped down flat on the floor, while the bear, like a train at full steam, went right over him. As soon as the bear was inside the barn, Sprīdītis sprang up and ran back out the door. Slam! – He shut the door, and the bear was trapped. The lord couldn't believe what he'd seen: "Amazing! Where did you get the courage to do that?"

"That was nothing," boasted Sprīdītis.

The lord was impressed but still did not want to give his daughter to such a strange little man. So he ordered him to kill the twelve robbers who were hiding in the forest: "Then you will have my daughter."

Unafraid, Sprīdītis again filled his pockets with stones. He went to the hideout, climbed a tree, and waited. At midnight the robbers returned. Sprīdītis watched and waited as they ate, drank and laughed over the day's plunder. After they settled drowsily around the fire, Sprīdītis threw a pebble and hit the chief on the head.

"Who did that? Which one of you dared to throw a rock at me?" Confused, the robbers just looked at each other and at the chief, but no one said a word. Then Sprīdītis threw another pebble and another, hitting the chief on the head each time.

Flying into a rage, the chief grabbed the closest robber, pulled him to his feet, and socked him in the eye. Pleading that he hadn't done anything wrong, the robber called to the rest of the gang for help. They all stood up, throwing punches every which way until they ended up in a bloody pile. Then Sprīdītis climbed down from the tree, cut off their heads and returned to the lord. "How did you do that?" he asked in disbelief.

"I threw a rock at one, then the other, then the third, and so on."

The lord was impressed, but still would not give up his daughter: "One last test. You must chase the occupying army out of my land. Then you will get your wish."

Gladly taking up the challenge, Sprīdītis said: "Bring me a white horse, and I'll take care of your enemy!"

"You heard him!" commanded the lord.

In no time, the steed appeared. Sprīdītis crawled up into the saddle and rode to meet the enemy, waving his sword with a battle cry that echoed through the trees.

The enemy commander, seeing such a little man waving a sword and riding at full speed on a white horse, began to tremble, "What kind of creature is this? He may be a spirit sent to punish us!" He hastily told his men to pack up and retreat. Seeing the apparition, they were only too glad to obey.

At last the lord decided that he had better keep his word, for how could he know what the strange little man would do to him if he didn't? And so Sprīdītis married the lord's daughter. Because of his bravery and intelligence, the lord made him a general, and to this day, the little man patrols the forest on his white steed, keeping the kingdom safe from bears and robbers.

Heating the Oven before Catching the Bird

(Putns vēl mežā, iesmu jau drāž)

One spring day, Ansīts, a fanciful young man, was gathering fire wood in the forest. He saw a rabbit crouching under a fir tree. This got him thinking: "After I catch this rabbit and sell it, I will get five copper coins. With that I shall buy a hen, which will lay eggs and hatch chickens. Then, I will sell the chickens and in time I will make enough money to buy myself an estate.

"Then I will take Greta for a wife, and we will name our first son Ansis after me. As soon as he's big enough, I'll put him to work on my estate, and I will strut around, a pipe between my teeth, giving orders like rich men do. Oh, yes! I will be admired by all!

"And I shall be strict with my servants and field hands. And, naturally, I won't have to work. Like all lords and masters, I will count my bulging sacks of grain and watch the men carry them into the granary. If they don't give me any trouble, I will be kind and merciful to my laborers. If my son whips or scolds them, I will clap my hands and shout: 'Ans! Ans! Stop! Don't hurt them!'"

Caught up in his daydream, Ansīts clapped his hands loudly with great conviction.

Startled by the noise, the rabbit scampered off into the woods as fast as his feet could carry him. And what did Ansīts do? Well, he just stood there as his castle in the clouds floated away.

The Hare and the Hedgehogs

(Zaķis un eži)

Once, long ago, a hedgehog and his brother decided to play a joke on a boastful hare who was strolling along the edge of a deep ditch, preening his whiskers and enjoying the sunshine.

After some debate, the hedgehogs decided to challenge the hare to a race. But first they had to figure out how they could win and embarrass Mr. Hare. So, they put their prickles together and determined what they would do. One brother crawled to the far end of the ditch and waited. The other brother waddled up to the hare and, lifting up his long snout, said:

"Listen here, Mr. Hare! You always brag about being a fast runner, but I am tempted to challenge you to a race and win."

"Oh, go on! I don't believe you. I would bet my whiskers on that!"

"If you win, you can pull ten needles out of my coat. If I win, I will pull out ten of your whiskers. Do you agree?"

"Sure!" the hare answered.

"Now, my friend, it seems right that you should run along the edge of the ditch, while I run at the bottom."

"Agreed!" said the hare. "Ready, set, go!"

The hare ran like the wind to the finish line. But when he reached the end mark, there was the hedgehog's brother, already waiting. "I win!" he taunted.

Confused, the hare plopped down in the grass. "I don't know how you beat me, but I concede defeat." He closed his eyes and let one of the brothers pull out ten whiskers. He then stuck five into his brother's upper lip and five into his own. And this is why, to this day, all hedgehogs have rabbit whiskers above their lips.

The Magic Ring

(Brīnumu gredzens)

Once upon a time, a dying father willed his son Žanis three silver coins.

"This is all I have to give you. When you are ready, use these coins to fulfill your destiny," he said.

"How will I know when I'm ready, Father?" asked the young Žanis.

"You will know in your heart when the time is right," he said. "You are meant to be more than a simple farmboy. One day, you will learn your true place." The father held his son's hand as he took his last breath.

"I don't understand, Father, but I will make you proud," he promised.

Because the boy was very young, his mother kept the money safely hidden. As soon as he turned sixteen and had grown quite tall and strong, he asked his mother for one of the coins.

"I want to go to town," he said.

"Well, since you are now grown, I will give you one of the coins. But be careful and spend it wisely!"

Žanis agreed and set off. On the way, he met an old woman carrying a puppy wrapped in her shawl.

"My son, will you please buy my dog?" she asked.

"Well," Žanis hesitated.

"You won't regret it," said the woman as the cute little dog wagged his tail and looked up pleadingly.

"How much?" asked Žanis.

"One silver coin," said the woman.

Looking into the woman's eyes, he felt he had no choice: "All right."

Žanis took the dog and, with some disappointment, headed for home: "I'll go to town another day," he thought.

When his mother saw his new pet, she was not at all pleased: "We hardly have enough food for ourselves, and you bring home a dog?"

"Please, *mammīt*! I had to help the old woman. And look how cute he is! Plus he will keep the foxes out of the chicken coop."

What could a mother do? She let him keep the dog, and life went on. But it was not long before her son became restless and again wanted to go to town. He asked his mother for another coin. "Okay, but be careful!" she warned.

*Žani*s set off, but before he reached town, he met the same woman on the road. This time she was holding a kitten: "My son, won't you please buy this kitten from me? You won't regret it."

"How much?"

"One silver coin."

Žanis felt compelled to help the old woman, even though it meant giving up his trip to town. "All right," he agreed.

He took the kitten home, and again his mother became very angry: "We are poor. We don't have any money or anything to eat. Why did you bring me another hungry mouth to feed?"

"Oh please, *māmiņ*! Look how sweet she is! Besides, she will keep our home free of mice."

"Well, all right," she reluctantly replied.

After a while, Žanis's feet itched for travel. "I do want to see the town," he thought. Knowing that his mother would not give him the last coin, he took it from her hiding place and away he went with doggy and kitty following behind. "This time I will not return until I have fulfilled my destiny and discovered the meaning of my father's final words," he vowed.

On the way, he again met the old woman on the road. Only now her hands were empty. She was just standing there as if waiting for Žanis to appear.

"Can I help you, ma'am?" Žanis asked.

"Look over there. Do you see that gravestone? Two feet under that is the tomb of a princess," she answered. "If you scratch the dirt away, you can lift the trapdoor and climb down to her casket. She has a precious ring on her finger made with the purest gold and the clearest amber that shines like the sun. I would like you to bring me that ring."

Žanis felt he had to obey the old woman. With the help of doggy and kitty, he scratched the dirt away and opened the trapdoor. He climbed down to the tomb and opened the casket. He quickly removed the ring from the princess's cold, lifeless finger, climbed back out, and presented it to the woman.

She examined the ring closely and then shyly asked, "My son, won't you please buy this ring? You won't be sorry."

"How much?"

"One silver coin."

"All right. It's my last," Žanis said and gave it to her. He accepted the ring and put it on.

The woman took the coin and before she disappeared told him that he should close the trap door right away. But Žanis wanted to go back and explore the tomb. No sooner had he reached bottom, when – bang! – the door closed down on him, and he was locked inside. He could neither push the door up, nor dig himself out. He was scared and didn't know what to do. He slumped down against the cold stone wall and put his mind to hard thinking, twisting the ring around and around on his finger, "I wish someone would come and save me!"

Suddenly, above the grave, six tiny men appeared. Doggy and kitty watched excitedly as they opened the trapdoor. The light shone in, and Žanis could see the blue sky above. He could hardly believe his eyes! "Where did you come from?" he asked the men in wonder.

"Your ring called us and we came," they said in chorus. "You see, as soon as you twirl the ring and make a wish, we must come at once and serve you."

"Well, well! That's wonderful! You may go now, but if I need you again, I'll twirl the ring and call you."

The little men disappeared, and Žanis, his dog and cat went on their way. Although he had no money left, he kept walking: "Father told me to fulfill my destiny, and that is exactly what I'm going to do."

The three friends traveled over hills and across valleys, through the woods and across fields. The nights were very cold. Žanis held kitty close to keep warm while doggy stood guard, protecting them from the wolves howling in the darkness. For three days they walked until finally they found themselves at the foot of a mountain, standing on a road lined with silver birches leading up to a golden castle.

"I can feel the castle pulling me forward," Žanis said. "I will find the meaning behind my father's words there, I'm sure. But we can't appear like this in front of the king!"

Žanis twirled the ring. Instantly, the six little men appeared. "What is your wish?" they asked.

"A new suit and a hat to match, for each of us."

The next instant Žanis found himself wearing a gold and red suit fit for a prince. Even his shoes were clean and shiny. Doggy and kitty were also dressed in finest clothes, a feather in their hats and silver bells tinkling on their collars.

"Now we are ready to face the future. Let's go!"

The trio walked down the promenade to the castle. As if the guards had been expecting them, they silently opened the gate and bowed. Žanis walked past them with his companions. One door after another opened before them, and soon they were standing in front of the king sitting upon his throne.

"I have come to learn the story of my existence and fulfill my destiny," Žanis said. He bowed as kitty and doggy lay down humbly at his feet. "We have been traveling for days and are very tired and hungry."

The king listened closely as Žanis described how he had come to this place, the cat, the dog, the old woman, and of course the ring. The king's daughter, who had been hiding behind a screen, came forward when he had finished his story. Imagining herself having walked with our hero through many kingdoms, she bowed before him. She gave him her hand, and he kissed it.

"I have been waiting for you," she said. "When I was very young, an old woman appeared in the garden while I was playing. She told me about a baby from a faraway kingdom who had been kidnapped and sold to a farmer and his wife. This is certainly the same old woman you described. She said, 'This child is destined to become your prince. One day you will marry and rule this kingdom.' 'But how will I recognize him?' I asked. 'He will be wearing a magic ring of gold and amber, a symbol of true love, heaven's greatest gift to mankind. When he puts the ring on your finger, your fate will be sealed.' You are wearing the ring the old woman described. You are my prince!"

Žanis listened in disbelief. "What about my parents?" he asked.

"Don't be angry," the princess answered. "They loved you as if you were their own, and they raised a fine man. But you were fated to leave them and take your rightful place on the throne. We will send for your mother, and she will live the rest of her days with us in the castle."

Knowing the princess's words to be true, Žanis took off the ring and slipped it on her finger. Twirling it around and around, he said, "I wish you would wear this ring, a symbol of unending love, forever."

And so, Žanis and the princess fulfilled their destiny. They ruled the kingdom for many years with the help of kitty and doggy, who kept the castle free of mice and the chicken coop safe from foxes.

A Contract with Wolves

(Līgums ar vilkiem)

A long time ago, an abundance of wolves lived in the northern woods. There were so many of them that they had become a constant threat to the farmers' sheep, killing them and taking them back to their dens. The farmers were so angry with the wolves that they'd shoot them on sight, even if they were just out for a walk or taking a drink from the stream. Finally, the slaughter became too much. The farmers and the wolves got together to try to come up with a solution.

"Look, you wolves, we cannot go on like this. You can't just sneak onto our land and kill our sheep," said the lead farmer.

"What are we supposed to do?" asked the head wolf. "We only take your sheep when we have to. Otherwise, we'd starve."

"Well, we've spent a fortune putting up fences and hiring dogs. Not to mention having to stand guard over our flocks all night."

"Do you think we enjoy sneaking around like common criminals? This used to be our land, and you have taken it over. We deserve at least half of this land and all the animals living on it," replied the wolf.

"You know, he has a point," said one of the other farmers. "Maybe we should just agree to give half of each sheep to the wolves. They're taking that much already. At least this way we won't have to lose sleep, and we can plan our profits better."

"That's fine by me," said another farmer. "What do you wolves think?"

The wolves put their noses together and discussed the offer.

"Agreed," said the head wolf. "You all must promise to give us exactly half of each sheep, and we promise to leave you in peace."

So the farmers and the wolves all shook hands to finalize the contract.

Then one day, when a farmer was ploughing up his fields, he saw a wolf with one of his sheep between his teeth: "Hey, what are you doing? We agreed to share each sheep equally. You are in clear breach of our contract. Now, give me back my sheep, and I'll give you your half as promised."

The wolf reluctantly dropped the sheep, and the farmer took it home. Then he started thinking, "The nerve of that wolf breaking our deal. I'm not going to give him his half. You just can't trust these wolves to keep their word."

So the farmer kept the sheep, and in the spring, she bore twin lambs. When the lambs were let out to graze, the wolf suddenly appeared: "I'm supposed to get half of each sheep. Now the farmer has three, and I have none. I knew these farmers couldn't be trusted." With that, the wolf took one of the lambs and carried it away.

The farmer, seeing one of his lambs had been stolen, flew into a rage: "That's it! These wolves are all alike! You make a deal, and they just break it!"

In the fall, the farmer slaughtered his lamb and the old sheep, but he refused to give the wolf his half. The neighbors, knowing the rules, became worried: "There's going to be trouble! This contract will only work if we all stick to it. Go give him his share, or we'll all pay the price."

Pressured by his fellow farmers, he finally agreed. He cut the old sheep in half and took it to the wolf. But he decided to keep the skin, "I deserve something for my trouble."

The wolf realized immediately that the farmer had kept the skin and became very angry: "I know I have no use for the skin – I don't even like to eat the skin – but that's beside the point! I'm supposed to get half, and that's what I'm going to get!"

The other wolves heard all this ruckus and, like the other farmers, pleaded with the wolf to accept what the farmer had given him: "Otherwise we will all suffer. It doesn't matter who started this. You must finish it."

The wolf would not listen. That night, he snuck onto the farmer's land, determined to get his fair share. But the farmer had already sunk the skin with the others in a barrel to ferment. Nevertheless, the wolf pulled the stinking skin out, tore it in half, put one half back and dragged the other half to his den in the woods.

Word of this standoff spread from one farmer to the next, from one wolf to the next, and soon the farmers were blaming the wolves and the wolves were blaming the farmers for breaking the contract. In no time, they were all at it again, the farmers shooting wolves on sight, and the wolves stealing sheep right and left. The peace was shattered because one farmer and one wolf could not give a little for the sake of all.

Those who are wise know, as the old saying goes: *Learn to live so that the wolf is fed, and the sheep is alive.*

The Catfish and the Trout

(Sams un ulis)

One spring day, a catfish was swimming through the depths of the Daugava. Going upstream, he soon tired out and stopped for a rest at the mouth of the Ogre river.

"The water looks much calmer in the Ogre," he thought. "Maybe life will be easier for me there." So he swam into the Ogre to have a look around.

The catfish hadn't gotten very far when he bumped into a trout.

"Hello, sir," the catfish said. "How is life here in these nice, cool waters? I'm from the Daugava, and I'm thinking about moving here."

Looking at this huge fish, the trout thought, "Oh no. If this gormandizer moves in here, he will surely gobble up all the eggs that we've carefully laid in the seaweed, not to mention the little minnows and smelts now swimming freely through our waters. We'll all become extinct within a year, especially when his friends start showing up. I can't let that happen."

Turning to the catfish, the trout said, "Brother, to be honest, life gets harder here from one day to the next. It's not like it used to be in old times. Do you think that we trout were always this small, the way you see me now? My grandfather was quite different from what I've become. His forehead alone was ten centimeters wide. But look at what's become of me. I guess our breed will just die out, if times don't get better for us.

"And don't think for a minute that you will find an easy life here. Wherever you try to float, you bump into a turtle, frog or another fish. If

I were you, I'd swim back to the Daugava, where there is lots of space. You can even float on your back like a leaf and nothing will bother you."

Hearing that the Ogre was not as nice as it seemed, the catfish changed his mind: "Thank you for the advice. I could have made a big mistake. My life in the Daugava isn't so bad. I'm going to head back."

And so, the catfish turned around, dove to the river bottom, and headed toward the Daugava. From then on, no one has seen a single catfish in the Ogre.

The Strange Reindeer

(Savādais briedis)

In a faraway land, there lived a king with his beautiful daughter. Naturally, she had no shortage of admirers. They came in droves from miles around, but she would not have anything to do with them. "There is no one as kind and handsome as my servant," she told her father. "And no one can play as beautifully on the lute as he. I shall marry only him, because I love only him."

"You're impossible!" The king shouted. "All these rich suitors, and you choose him? I refuse to have a poor, lowly farmhand as a son-in-law, and I expect you to obey me. You are a princess, but I am the king!"

"Oh father, please leave me alone," she implored and walked away.

"All right," muttered the king. "It looks like I will have to deal with this in my own way. I'm not going to get anywhere with her."

The king acted quickly. He called his guards: "Take that servant back to where he came from!"

The king believed his daughter would soon forget about her beloved servant with all the other suitors vying for her attention and, for a while, it seemed to work. The princess did not complain, but that was only because she knew her true love would find his way back to her.

The servant, meanwhile, was back at his father's hut. But he was neither gloomy nor idle. Instead, just like the princess thought, he was busy plotting his return. Finally, he came upon a most unusual idea: "I will carve a huge reindeer out of this piece of wood," he told his father as he was dragging home a large oak log. "This will win me the hand of the princess once and for all!"

Not wasting any time, the servant took out his tools and began carving. He worked day and night, night and day, only stopping to eat and sleep. Finally, the reindeer was finished. Gleaming and sturdy, no one could tell that the servant had also carved out a hollow space where its stomach should be. Then he took his lute and climbed up into the hollow space. Before closing himself in, he told his father to take the reindeer, with him inside, to the castle as a gift to the king.

So the father loaded the reindeer onto his cart and set off. When he arrived at the castle, all the servants, suitors, noblemen and noblewomen gathered around. No one had ever seen such a beautifully carved reindeer.

As the crowd grew, the servant, still inside, took up his lute and started to play. He sang so sadly, so mournfully, so purely, that everyone was moved to tears. Lured by the music, the king and princess came out of the castle and listened, and they, too, were charmed. "What an unusual gift! Where did it come from?" the king asked. But the servant's father had long disappeared into the crowd.

The king was very pleased with his toy. Proud and flattered, he boasted, "Behold, my dear subjects, what marvels can be found in the big wide kingdom I rule!"

But the princess? She knew what the reindeer was and who it was from as soon as she heard her beloved's voice. Pleadingly, impatiently, she put her arms around her father's neck and begged him to let her have the wooden reindeer. "I love it!" she said. "I've never had such a wonderful toy, and you know how lonesome I've been these days." The king guessed for whom she was lonesome and thought that if he gave her the reindeer, she would forget the servant that much sooner. And so the huge toy was taken into the princess's chamber.

What joy! What happiness! After such a long, lonesome time, the young people were together again. The good and faithful servant played and sang, and when the pair heard someone coming, the servant hid inside the reindeer until it was safe to come back out. In such manner a week went by.

The king had never seen his daughter so happy, and, of course, this made him happy too. But then, one day, the cook, who also loved the princess and had always been jealous of the servant, said to the king: "I hate to disturb your digestive system, but something is not right in your daughter's room. Because, you see, the deer never needs to be wound up. How can it keep singing and playing without a wind-up mechanism? Something is fishy, I'm telling you."

"I never noticed that," said the king. "Let's open it up and see what's inside."

The next day, a carpenter was called. He took a sharp saw and an ax and he, the king and the cook stormed into the princess's room, scaring her half to death. The carpenter cut and sawed, sawed and cut, until the servant had no choice but to reveal himself. He finally crawled out of the deer's belly, pale as a ghost.

Oh, my goodness! What rage, what language, what madness! The king had not made such scene since he was a young prince: "Lock that wretch up in the tower!" The guards tied the servant up and dragged him away.

The princess was so scared of what her father might do next that she quickly climbed out the window and ran. The servant could only helplessly watch her from his barred window, praying nothing would happen to her, "Please be safe, my love!"

As soon as the princess reached the edge of the lake, a great black storm cloud appeared directly over her, blocking out the sun. It seemed to pull her up into the air as a puppet on a string. The cloud floated across the water and hovered over an island, far in the middle of the lake. Then, as suddenly as it had come, the cloud disappeared, and the princess was alone and stranded on the island.

The king, meanwhile, was very distressed. He did not know where his daughter might be and what could have happened to her. He worried for two days and two nights. He looked for her here, and he looked for her there, but he found her nowhere. Then, on the third night, he had a dream. A beautiful woman flew down to his bedside and whispered in his ear: "Set the lute player free. He will find your daughter."

In the morning the king woke up, instantly remembering the woman who had spoken so gently to him. She had looked much like his deceased wife. He felt sorry for his child, who had no mother and who soon might perish if he did not help her. "My dear, pretty daughter! I must save her even if I have to set the scoundrel free," the king decided. He quickly marched up the tower steps and asked his once-faithful servant, "Can you help me find my daughter?"

"Set me free and give me a boat. I will bring your daughter home," the young man promised.

The king didn't understand why a boat was needed, but he would agree to anything to save his daughter. And so he let the servant out. Taking his lute, the servant hurried to the shore, untied the boat, and sailed to the island. He found the princess, quickly put her in the boat, and they sailed back to the king. The servant serenaded his princess all the way home. When the king saw the boat nearing the shore, he was struck by how happy the young lovers were and, in spite of himself, exclaimed, "What a beautiful pair they make!"

So, at last, the king gave his blessing, and the princess and commoner were united. The reindeer also became part of the family, and at Christmastime, he was decorated with tinsel and ornaments, a symbol of love and happiness.

The Poor Man's Fortune
(Nabaga vīra laime)

Once upon a time, there were two farmers: one rich, the other poor. As the poor man walked around his fields one Sunday evening, he saw someone in the rich man's field cutting hay. He walked up to the strange figure and asked, "Who are you, and why are you working on a holy day?"

"I am the rich man's fortune, and I must add my blessing to his labors before the work week begins."

"Why don't you ever come to bless me?" the poor farmer asked.

"I cannot help you because you were not destined to be a farmer. Your fortune is in business. Your wife has a fine striped cloth packed away in her closet. She made this cloth from the special wool of your own sheep. Grow your flock, make more wool, and spin more cloth. Then take your wares to market. With patience and work, you and your wife will find success."

The farmer did as he was advised and, before long, he became so rich that he had to count his money by the bushel. But he did not have a bushel basket, so he had to borrow one from his neighbor.

The rich neighbor had been watching these events unfold and wondered, "Why does he need a bushel basket? What does he have to measure and weigh?" To discover the answer, he pressed some tar into the bottom of the basket and then gave it to his neighbor.

When the basket was returned, the rich farmer found a coin stuck in the tar. "Sure enough," he thought, "he has bushels of money!" This really surprised him, for the neighbor's fields were as poor-looking as ever. "What is that ne'er-do-well doing?" he wondered and hurried over to him to find out. "How did you make so much money in such a short time?" he asked.

"Why, I earned it by doing good business – by selling and trading."

The rich man, not wanting to be outdone, went back home, determined to get into some kind of trade as soon as he could. But what happened? By concentrating on business, he neglected his farming, which had been blessed by fortune. After trading all his goods, he was unable to manage his business. He soon lost everything and became very poor indeed.

The Fox and the Pipe

(Lapsa ar pīpi)

One evening, a fox was sneaking around a chicken coop, hoping to snatch an egg or two. "Every night the same routine," he griped. "I'm getting sick and tired of stealing eggs, digging for mice, rooting through fields. I'd be better off draped as a stole around some rich woman's neck. I need some excitement in my life!"

Just then, he tripped over something. "What's this?" he wondered, looking more closely. "It's the farmer's pipe! I've seen him smoking it many times. You know, I've always wanted to smoke a pipe."

So the fox crept into a hay barn and lit the pipe as he'd seen the farmer do it. As he puffed, the smoke rose in a cloud around his head, and he began to cough. His eyes started watering, and he couldn't see. Then a spark accidentally fell from the pipe onto the dry straw, which quickly caught on fire. The fox tried to put the flames out by beating them with his tail, but his tail also caught on fire, burning the fur down to the skin. Then he tried to spit on the fire, thinking that would put it out. But he got too close, and all his whiskers burned off.

As the fire grew, the farmer smelled the smoke and ran to the barn with a pail of water. Luckily, he managed to put out the fire in time, and no one was hurt.

Embarrassed, the fox stuck his hairless tail between his legs and dragged himself down to his den. As he licked his wounds, he thought, "When I said I wanted excitement, I didn't mean I wanted to nearly die in a fire! There must be something else I could do that wouldn't be so dangerous. You know, I've always wanted to learn how to dance . . ."

Three Admonitions of a Father

(Trīs tēva padomi)

Lying on his deathbed, a father called his son to his side to give him some final advice: "My boy, always remember what I am about to tell you. One, do not go visiting often, for people will quickly grow tired of you. Two, do not swap horses in the marketplace, for you will end up on foot. Three, do not take a wife from far away, for your marriage will be a disaster."

The son scratched his head and tucked his father's advice away inside. After the father's death, the orphaned young man got to thinking about his final words. "I'm going to put his advice to the test," he resolved.

The next day, the young man went to visit his neighbors who lived many acres away. They were happy to see the lonesome, grieving son and treated him to delicious pancakes. The next week, the young man came again, and again the wife made a batch of pancakes for him, but not as many as before. She also left out a couple important ingredients. The third time the man came, the pancakes were cold, and the fourth time they tasted terrible. On the young man's fifth visit, the neighbors were too busy to even greet him and gave him nothing to eat or drink. The sixth time, the irritated wife handed him a stale loaf of bread with a jug of fermented buttermilk and didn't say a word.

The young man bit into the loaf of bread and left, taking the rest home. He hid the loaf inside a finely carved box. As he went to sleep that night, he said to himself, "Father's first rule was correct. Tomorrow I'll test the second."

The next morning, bright and early, the orphan took his horse to the market and traded it for another. He kept trading for some time, going to different markets until, at last, he ended up with a lame mare that could hardly walk. On the way home she collapsed and died. Our hero skinned the mare, took the hide, and walked home. He made some leather goods and put one piece in his box, next to the stale loaf of bread, "Father was right on two counts. Now I've got to test the third."

Early the next Sunday, the sadder but wiser man started out across the countryside in search of a wife. He looked and looked, stopping at different houses and towns until he found a girl standing in front of a well-tended farmhouse. She was pretty and walked so gracefully that it seemed her feet hardly touch the ground. The young man looked at her, and she looked at him, and – it was love! In all sincerity, he asked her to marry him, and she accepted. Quite smitten with each other, they could hardly wait to be united. They agreed to make the announcement the following Sunday at the groom's church. Even the future in-laws approved and allowed him to spend the night in their attic, on the condition that he left the next morning before their daughter awoke.

"All right," he said and happily went to bed thinking only of the beautiful girl in her pretty room. But before falling asleep he suddenly remembered his father's last words and his reason for looking for a bride clear across the countryside. "I have to stay the course and heed my father's advice," he said to himself.

The only way he could be sure that this young lady would make a good wife was to spend more time at her house and observe her daily behavior. So, he pretended to leave the house as agreed, but then backtracked and hid where he could watch her in secret. However, it was Sunday. "Nobody works on a Sunday, so she'll be as pretty and charming as when I first saw her. I'll stay on through Monday," he resolved.

On Monday morning, everyone, including the girl's aged parents, went out to work in the fields. "But where is she?" the young man wondered. He did not see her in the morning; he did not see her at noon. So he snuck into the empty house, afraid she might have fallen and needed help. He looked all around and finally opened the door to her room. He noticed that the apron she wore on Saturday was lying on the floor. He stopped. He looked and listened. He thought he heard soft snoring noises coming from behind the curtain. He peeked – and sure enough – there was the girl, asleep in her bed. "And this is the girl I have chosen to be my wife and the manager of my household!"

He quickly grabbed the apron and ran home. He put the apron in his box with the bread and the piece of leather and shut the lid. Then he went about his day as usual, waiting calmly for the following Sunday, when he was expected to announce his engagement. But he did not go to church; instead, the deacons, the girl's parents, and the bride arrived at his house in a fine carriage to pick him up. The young man had no intention of marrying this girl, so he hid in a cupboard, watching them all look for him and enjoying the whole charade.

While they were searching, the mother came upon the carved box. "What's this?" she wondered. Our hero then revealed himself, hopping out of the cupboard and surprising everyone. "This box contains my most precious things," he said.

"Let's see – please!" begged the girl, looking as pretty as ever. The young man almost fell for her all over again, but he hardened his heart and thought of his father. "Well, all right, you asked for it!" He opened the lid and there, for all to see was the stale bread, the piece of leather, and – the apron.

"Sweetheart," said the girl, "how did my apron get inside your box?"

"You see, honey, this box – this case – is very important to me. It contains the evidence proving that what my father advised me was sound and true. These three things may not mean anything to you, but they have made me wise and so far have protected me from making serious mistakes. I'll tell you what I've learned." And he listed the three pieces of advice his father had given him.

When the girl heard the third point about the dangers of picking a wife from a far country, and realized it pertained to her, she was so embarrassed that she ran out of the house and hid inside the carriage. Shamefaced, the parents followed, and the humiliated family started their long journey home.

A Ram and a Wolf

(Auns un vilks)

One day, while roaming through the meadow, a small ram with large horns became separated from the other sheep. Bleating, the poor thing ran back and forth through the tall grass, trying to find his flock.

He was so panicked that he ran smack into a big wolf. Grinning and licking his chops, the wolf howled at the sheep: "Stop and prepare to be eaten!"

"That's just fine!" the ram laughed. "I have been running around all day. I am alone and death would be a relief. Go to the bottom of the hill, stand there, face me, and open your mouth wide. I will run down the hill and straight into your stomach."

The wolf could hardly wait to gobble up this delicious ram. He trotted down the slope, turned around, and opened his mouth as wide as his jaws would go. The ram, set himself on the mark, and counted *one, two, three . . . Ready! Set! Go!*

The ram charged like a stone out of a slingshot. Horns first, he butted squarely into the wolf who fell backwards and lay as if dead. The ram turned away and laughed. Down in the valley, hiding in the bushes were the sheep who had seen it all. They hailed the brave, little ram as the hero of the day.

When the wolf came to, he shook his head in confusion. "That was some knock-down. I've never seen so many stars before my eyes. I'm not sure if the ram ran through me or around me, but one thing is for sure, he isn't in my stomach."

The Golden Wings

(Zelta spārni)

Once, a long time ago, before there were airplanes and spaceships, and only birds flew about in the air, there lived a king. He was a good king, and he wanted to make sure the people were happy with his rule, so he sent a servant out to travel the land and learn what his subjects were saying about him.

This job pleased the servant, for he not only got a chance to see the world but also to hear all kinds of gossip, though very little about the king. "What can I say about the king?" was the typical response. "The king is as kings are." Or: "I'm not interested in politics. I leave the king alone, and he leaves me alone."

Finally, by chance, the servant overheard a conversation between two sorcerers. "If the king gave me five hundred tons of wood to burn, and the wind was right, I could produce a fish of pure silver," said one.

Challenging him, the other sorcerer boasted: "If the king gave me a thousand tons of wood, I could produce a pair of golden wings."

The servant thought the king would be very happy to get a pair of golden wings, so he went straight to the second sorcerer and said, "Come with me!" The two returned to the castle and went to the king. Hearing the promise of golden wings, he eagerly granted the sorcerer a thousand tons of wood.

As soon as the wood was gathered, the sorcerer and the servant lit the kindling. Then they piled one log on top of another until they had a huge bonfire. When the flames were licking the treetops, the sorcerer stood back and raised his hands. He closed his eyes and began humming in a low voice at first, then louder and louder and louder. When he'd finished his incantation, to the amazement of the servant, he rose into the air, spun around three times, and came back down to earth. "Now we wait," he told the servant.

The two watched the fire burn for what seemed like an eternity. Finally, only a pile of ashes was left. Once the ashes cooled down, they took a shovel and started digging. Sure enough, they found a beautiful pair of golden wings under all the dust. Oh, how the wings shone and glistened!

The servant was only too glad to take the wings to the king. The king was very pleased, but he had no idea what to do with them. So, he hung them up in his wardrobe. Then, one day, he prepared to take a trip to the seaside and asked his son to come along. But the prince had grown very curious about the wings, so he stayed behind, saying he had a headache.

After the king and all his attendants had gone, the prince went into his father's chamber and took the golden wings from the wardrobe. Wanting to see what these wings could do, he twisted them this way and that, tying them on and off until he finally attached them to his arms. He admired himself in the mirror, thinking he looked like the angel Gabriel.

Suddenly, he rose up in the air, at first flying around the room and then out the window. He soared higher and higher, marveling at the tiny houses and trees below. He flew for three days and three nights. At the end of the third day, he heard a strange voice calling him from on high: "Make three turns on your right side only, and you will land safely."

The prince did as he was told and – behold! – the wings took him down to earth, right in front of the castle gate of a foreign king. The prince hid the wings under a bush and approached the guards. Not knowing where he was or how he was going to get back home, he said, "I would like to work for the king, please."

"That's good," said one of the guards. "We need a shepherd."

And so, the prince agreed to tend the strange king's flock until he could figure out what to do next. Humble and kind, he didn't mind the job as long as the weather was fine. But when it rained, the prince became very discouraged: "I'll never get home at this rate! I'm so lonely with only cows and sheep to talk to."

Then, one day, the king's daughter stole into the meadow, curious to see this new shepherd. She hid behind a tree, thinking he wouldn't see her, but the prince soon spotted the red hem of her skirt blowing out from behind the tree. He walked up to her.

"Can I help you, princess?" he shyly asked.

"Oh, hello," the princess nervously answered. "I just came to welcome you to our kingdom. I don't have many friends, you see, and I have been lonely here in the castle."

"I feel the same. No matter how much I talk to the animals, they never answer me back," he joked.

The princess laughed, feeling a flush of happiness fill her heart. The prince, also smitten, wanted to learn everything there was to know about her. And so the two talked about this and that, about everything and nothing. She came out the next day and the next, and they laughed and joked, so blinded by love they became careless and didn't realize that they were being watched.

On the third day, the king was told that the princess had been spending time with the new shepherd. Very protective of his only daughter, he called the two before him.

"My girl, you are a princess. It is not proper for you to be spending time with this lowly shepherd. And you," he turned to the prince, "I am banishing you from my kingdom. I command you to leave at once!"

"But father, we love each other! Please let him stay!"

"Out of the question!" the king bellowed.

Realizing this was his one and only chance, the prince grabbed the princess by the hand and the two fled out the door through the gate and to the bush where the golden wings were hidden. He quickly pulled them out and attached them securely on his back. The princess saw the gold and, amazed, watched her shepherd tie, turn, and twist them into place. Then he held her tightly, and together they rose into the air, leaving the king's guards and barking dogs far behind.

The wings carried the lovers higher and higher, in and out of the clouds. They flew around for three days and three nights. On the third day, the prince heard the same good voice calling from on high: "Turn yourself three times on the right side, and you will land safely."

The prince did as he was told, and – behold! – the wings took him down to earth, right before his father's door.

"At last, I am home!" the prince exclaimed. He looked into the princess's eyes and promised: "Together we will live as husband and wife and rule the kingdom fairly, as my father has."

The king, seeing his boy had returned, was surprised and overcome with happiness, embracing him, kissing him, and welcoming the princess as she cried tears of joy. Soon a most splendid wedding took place, and they all lived happily ever after. And the golden wings? The king kept them safely locked in his wardrobe, for he did not want his son or his new daughter-in-law to ever leave him again.

Bēdu, manu lielu bēdu,
Es par bēdu nebēdāju!
Liku bēdu zem akmeņa,
Pāri gāju dziedādams.

Sorrow, sorrow, pain and trouble!
I won't let you hold me down!
Put my troubles 'neath a boulder
Walked across it singing songs.